THE LITTLE BLΛ

Chicago Edition

A Shopping Directory of Black-owned
(African Descent)
Fashion & Retail Stores Around The Windy City!

By Melody Boykin, Edited by Daé Destino,
Foreword by Jermikko Shoshonna

Copyright

Printed in Chicago, IL

First Printing: January 2021
Library of Congress Control Number: 2020925205
The Little Black Boutique Guide (Chicago Edition)
North America; Online
By Melody Boykin, Edited By Daé Destino,
Foreword by Jermikko Shoshanna
Book Design By Dewwond Mapp Kentyla Art Designs

125 pgs., 5in by 7in
ISBN 978-1-7353168-0-2 (Paperback)

visit the website: www.blackfashionweekusa.com/boutiqueguide/

To order The Little Black Boutique Guide or for information on using
copies as corporate gifts e-mail us at info@blackfashionweekusa.com
CC: Thelitteblackboutiqueguide@gmail.com

Black Fashion Week
The Little Black Boutique Guide
PO BOX 7579
Chicago, IL 60680

This Book is Sponsored By

B FRAGRANCED

TABLE OF CONTENTS

5   *Foreword*

7   *Acknowledgements*

9   *Introduction*

13   *Chicago Boutique Guide*

97   *Chicagoland Art Galleries*

97   *Chicagoland Bookstores*

98   *Chicagoland Beauty Supply Stores*

99   *Chicagoland Nail/Spa Boutiques*

101 *Chicagoland Cultural Institutions*

101 *Chicagoland Cafés & Restaurants*

107 *Boutique Side Trips Across the Nation*

112 *Body Figure Type*

115 *Fashion Glossary*

118 *Maps*

120 *Photo Credit*

121 *Selected Bibliography*

122 *Book Index*

Foreword

There is a great value of knowledge in my friend Melody's book "The Little Black Boutique Guide Chicago Edition. I am honored to write this foreword upon Melody's request.

Over four decades ago, when I became Chicago's first person of color in the Fashion Design and Manufacture business selling to retailers, I was out there alone. I often had to tuck myself away from those who would not accept my talent because of my skin color. Now, fast forward to the year 2020 and there's an African American fashion guide book working to tell the world our businesses exist, the types of clothing we specialize in, and where we are located.

I met this very caring young lady years ago and, although it took her many attempts to gain my attention, she never gave up. When I finally agreed to meet her I could see she was very determined to make sure that we as African American fashion artists would not fade into the night unknown, so she started Black Fashion Week.

Black Fashion Week showcases talented African American designers, many from Chicago retailers, hair and makeup artists, photographers and models mainly during the month of February via their multiple fashion shows. Wherever there's an opportunity for Blacks in the world of fashion, Melody makes sure we are aware and included.

Melody's love of seeking out and showcasing talented African Americans in all creative areas of fashion makes her the perfect person to write this guide. There is the old saying, "If a tree falls in the forest and no one was there, did it make a noise?"

Melody, thank you for making sure others are here to hear us make fashion noise. This book will give you knowledge, pride, and resources. "The more we know, the more we grow."

Jermikko Shoshanna, CEO Chicago's first and longest established Fashion Designer/Manufacturer/Inventor.

www.jermikko.com

Photo courtesy of Jermikko Shoshanna
Photography: Fred Brown Photograhy
Model: Kai

6

Acknowledgements

I would like to thank God for giving me the vision and patience to complete this book and for the desire to help spotlight the contributions of the many Black business owners featured throughout the publication. Thank you to my wonderful parents for birthing me. Thanks to my mom, Denise Robinson (d. 2013), who taught me how to fight for a cause. And my dad, Burnett Boykin, for supporting me in my many adventures over the years. Special thanks to my stepmom, Joy Boykin, who introduced me to the world of fashion at a young age and encouraged me to pursue a career in fashion. A special acknowledgement to my two-year-old son, Joseph Royal Stanford, for keeping mommy on her toes. To my entire family: Thank you for your continued support!

I would like to thank my dynamic professional team of supporters who have stood by me during the creation of this book project over the last few years. Thank you, Daé Destino, my awesome behind the scenes editor for many projects including the birth of the Black Fashion Week events. Special thanks to celebrity designers, Etu Evans and Jermikko Shoshanna, for your continued support during my fashion journey over these last several years. Thank you to my personal and professional photographer, Darel White, of Darel Photography who has performed many photo-shoots and captured some of the best images for me over the last ten years, including images in this book project. A special thank you to Travon Christon Printis of TCP Photography who shared my vision in capturing local boutiques with your video camera. A special thanks to Dewwond Mapp of Kentyla Arts Designs for formatting this publication and for your superior work as a multimedia professional. Thank you to the super talented celebrity makeup artist Jacqueline Andrews Amaker (makeup By JShuntay) for always making me feel like a glamor girl. A special thanks to Effortless Boutique, also featured in the publication, for supplying the wardrobe for the book cover of this publication. I also send many thanks to the talented 2016 Black Fashion Week | USA model Christina Clark, who accepted the invitation to be a featured model in this book. Thank you to Marilyn Jones, owner and founder of B Fragranced - Embellish by ME. Thank you Georgeina Driver, owner of Luv That Scrub, Tonya Byrd-Neeley of Wired The Design Boutique, and Catrina Hagel of Ladies Consignment Boutique for sponsoring this publication, and for your support of this highly anticipated book project.

8

Introduction

Chicago is a city that is booming with diverse art and cultural institutions consisting of restaurants, art galleries, museums, churches, beauty salons, dance studios, and fashion establishments. My cultural senses were enlightened while patronizing a variety of these fascinating businesses –many within Black communities. My recent tour of Black-owned brick and mortar fashion businesses has not only left me knowledgeable, but empowered and inspired by the history and contributions made by Black people in fashion. I became instantly mesmerized with the growth of Black fashion businesses within Black and non-Black communities in Chicago. For example, during my discovery of some of Chicago's South Side boutiques, I learned that many were amongst the first African American owned businesses within the city. These first boutiques include Maxine's Boutique, Classy Lady, Sullivan Fashions, Wesley's Shoe Corral, and Island Furs –and all of these have honorably stood the test of time within the highly competitive industry of fashion. Maxine's Boutique was blessed with the task of selling their shoes and accessories to be included in the world's largest travelling fashion show, Ebony Fashion Fair, created by the late fashion icon Eunice Johnson, co-founder of Ebony Magazine. This colorful fashion discovery of classic and contemporary Black-owned businesses has left me with an unforgettable cultural experience rich in art, history, and fashion.

It is with great privilege and delight to present this shopping guide that highlights hundreds of Black-owned businesses! That is: African, African American, African Caribbean or descendants of the African Diaspora. These boutiques are growing rapidly around the Windy City in neighborhoods such as Bronzeville, Hyde Park, Beverly, the West Loop, the South Loop, and a few suburban townships. Whether you are a tourist or a Chicago native, this quick and easy guide will lead you to explore unique, one-of-a-kind Black-owned fashion boutique businesses in and around Chicago!

Key Guide

This book by no means represents all of the wonderful Black-owned stores not mentioned or featured in this book in the Chicago land area and abroad. The author has selected stores via her research for which information was readily available. Every boutique featured in this book has something unique to offer as no two stores are alike in concept and merchandise offerings. The Author hopes you will like the stores selectedto be featured in this publication and forgive any omissions.

Any indication of curent size ranges, price ranges, merchandise categories,business hrs and instore discountslisted etc., mentioned is merely to help define the store featured and can only be indicative of what information was available at the time of writing, and therefore may be subject to changes upon publication of this book. Please note this book publishing date was released during the 2020 Coranavirus world global health pandemic and any updates of business contact info including hrs of operation are at the sole discretion of all business owners listed within the publication. Unless otherwise stated, all stores take cash, and credit cards as payment for goods and service.

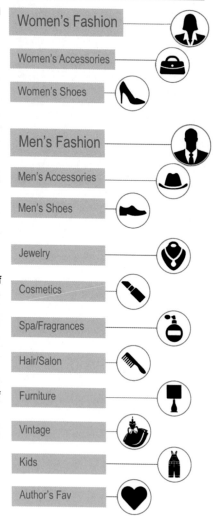

Women's Fashion

Women's Accessories

Women's Shoes

Men's Fashion

Men's Accessories

Men's Shoes

Jewelry

Cosmetics

Spa/Fragrances

Hair/Salon

Furniture

Vintage

Kids

Author's Fav

PRICE RANGES

$-$$	$1-$99
$$-$$$	$99-$999
$$$-$$$$	$999-$9999

This unique one of a kind guide features:

- Black Boutiques organized by neighborhoods
- An easy to read key guide to help navigate which stores are fit for your budget, size, and style of
- fashion
- A brief body figure guide for women
- A basic fashion glossary
- A brief reference list to nearby Black owned cultural institutions including art galleries, theaters,
- museums ,cafes, restaurants , beauty supply stores and nail/spa salons
- Discounts on first time purchases at select stores listed in this publication.

With these full shopping guide features, it is my hope that you explore all of the fascinating places to see, sip & shop, making The Little Black Boutique Book the go-to guide for shopping Black-owned fashion businesses in Chicago and beyond!

KHAM'RYN B SHOES & ACCESSORIES

Kham'ryn B Shoes & Accessories

Following in the footsteps of their father who once
owned a chain of stores throughout Chicago and
Indiana, the trendy sisters Karyn and Khamiya
are the co-owners of Kham'ryn B. Shoes and
have styled the soles of women and men for more
than a decade. Their shoe store located on the city's
Southwest Side is a popular staple for some of the most
exclusive international designer and couture shoe brands from various countries
such as Italy and Paris. Recently, they added fashion apparel which includes
clothing for women and men, unique formal attire for prom, and wedding tuxedos
to their legendary shoe assortment, thus staying true to their fashion motto "A
Look, A Style, An Image".

Address| 8301 S. Ashland Ave, Chicago, IL 60620
Hours| Mon-Sat: 11am-7pm | Sun:Closed
Phone| Phone: 773-881-3296
Email| khamrynbshoes@aol.com
Price Range|$-$$$
Size Range| S-XL | **Women Shoes:** 6-11| **Men:** 7-15
Website| www.khamrynb.com/
FB| Kham'ryn B.Shoes & Accessories
IG| khamrynb and @kbmen
First Time Shoppers Discount with Book | %15 in store |use code LBBG Online

Nearby Stores not featured in the this publication:

Allyson Mari| 7908 S. Artesian Chicago, IL 60652 | 773-313-9032
www.allysonmari.com/
Cannon's T-Shirts & More| 347 E. 75th St, Chicago, IL 60619| 872- 303-3644
Culture Connection| 400 W. 71st St, Chicago, IL 60621 | 773- 527-6015
www.cultureconnection360.com
GQ Gentlemen Boutique| 7149 S. State St, Chicago, IL 60619 | 773-966-4383
www.shopgqgentlemen.com
The Fashion Revival Boutique| 209 E.w 75th St Chicago, IL 60619| 773-234-0882
www.thefashionrevival.com

BELLĒ UP

CULTURE CLOSET

DEZ DEME HOUSE OF STYLES

ISLAND FURS

Bellē Up

When owner Jamenda McCoy was frustrated with the lack of clothing options at popular stores during her pregnancies in 2005 and 2007, she decided to create a store built for moms by a mom and catapulted Bellē Up in 2009. Located on the Southside of Chicago in the Beverly community, the store offers an array of fashionable, comfortable maternity clothing apparel for moms to be and their little ones. Bellē Up also carries chic apparel for non-mothers and a cool assortment of merchandise such as candles, journals, and small home décor products.

Address| 1915 W. 103rd Street, Chicago, IL 60643
Hours| Mon-Fri: 10am-6pm | Sat: 10am-5pm|Sun:Closed
Phone| 773-233-CHIC-2442
Email| info@belleup.com
Price Range| $$-$$$
Size Range| XS-3X
Website| www.BelleUp.com
FB| Belleupchicago | @belleupchicago
IG| Belleup
First Time Shoppers Discount With Book | N/A

Culture Closet

Home of the "Size Sexy Clothing" brand, a new line dedicated to promoting health & fitness and all things chic for curvy girls, Culture Closet formerly Curve Culture Boutique has earned its glam hat on the Southside of Chicago for curvaceous women. This specialty boutique owned by Quina Allen, a native of the community, features everything from classy, sexy social pieces, must-have jewelry and accessories. Culture Closet Boutique also carries intimate apparel along with popular shapewear like Spanx and hosiery from Chicago's Ice Cream Lady "Haute Fishnet Hosiery". With their affordable price points, women are bound to leave the store with more than an arm-full of colorful, confident pieces they can call "curve culture." The boutique has been featured on VH1, Bravo, HGTV and Full Figured Fashion Week, and has no plans of playing shy when it comes to the latest fashions for voluptuous sistahs.

Address| 2140 W. 95th Street Chicago, IL 60643
Hours| Mon-Fri:11am-7pm|Sat:11am-8pm
Phone| 773-941-5233
Email| onlinesales@curvecultureboutique.com
Price range| $$-$$$
Size Range| 1x-3x (12-20)
Website| www.culturescloset.com
FB| CurveCultureBoutique
IG| Curveculture
First Time Shoppers Discount| N/A

Dez DeMe House of Styles

Known for their excellent customer service and chic clothing, Dez DeMe House of Styles is one of Chicagoland's fastest growing boutique.The store carries jewelry, shoes and clothing catered to the young social diva ages 25 and up. Owner Menia believes "No diva should be left behind", and she works hard to ensure this is true with in-house fashion stylists, her signature Dez Diva Club, in-store special events, and a chic assortment of brands. What's admirable about this boutique is the unique fashion magazine collage embedded in the store's floor. It's the only type of store décor of its kind in Chicago and an absolute must-see that will immediately unleash the style diva in you.

Address| 2142 W. 95th Street Chicago IL, 60643
Phone| 773-789-2859
Hours| Tue-Sat:12pm-7pm |Sun: Closed
Email| customerservice@dezdeme.com
Price range| $$-$$$
Size Range| S-3X
Website: www.dezdeme.com/
FB|DezDeMe
IG| Dezdeme
First Time Shoppers Discount| 15% code vip15

Nearby Stores not featured in the this publication:

Crazy Creative Boutique | 2146 W.95th St, Chicago, IL 60643|708- 713-6622
https://www.crazycreativeboutique.com/

Island Furs

There's only a few African American furriers in the country and Chicago's home to one of them. Co-owned by Mr Gerard Brown and the late Mr. James the owners dedicated their careers to dressing business professionals, entertainers, and luxury shoppers for over 29 years in the best furs and luxury coats. This store is definitely the destination island for all things quality. The store has been blessed to offer its clients leather shearlings in regular and full-figure sizes. Also available are men's and women's cold weather accessories such as handbags, hats, scarves and chic phone cases. Complimentary fur services are provided such as cleanings, repairing, custom design, restyling, and storage. The shop is popular among church officials, business professionals and many celebrities over the years including Ron Isley, and former radio personality Angela Martin of Inspirational WGRB-1390's Angela & Mark In the A.M. morning radio show. The family operated business is a leader in the fur industry and the epitome of all things lux in outerwear.

Address| 1827 W 103rd Street, Chicago, IL 60643
Phone| 773-881-3877
Hours| Mon-Fri:10am-6pm | Sat:10am-5pm
Email| islandfurs@aol.com
Price range| $$-$$$$$$
Size Range| All Sizes
Website: | www.islandfurs.com
FB| Island Furs
IG| Island Furs
First time shoppers discount| N/A 40-70% off selected merchandise every day

Near by Stores not featured in the this publication:

Alpha 2 Omega | 1838 W 95th St, Chicago, Illinois 60643 | Phone:773-445-9044
Djenne Collection | 1759 W 95th St, Chicago, IL 60643 | 773- 445-0525
www.djennecollection.com/
Hobdy Shoe Repair | 1322 W 95th St, Chicago, IL 60643 | 773- 238-6655
Lourdes Hats & Accessories | 2243 W 95th St, Chicago, IL 60643 | 773-445-6615

Glam Fashion Love Boutique

Pamela Marie Bridal Boutique

Pamela Marie Bridal Boutique

Pamela Marie Bridal Boutique, owned by
Pamela Perkins, is a luxurious full-service bridal
salon once located in Chicago's Bridgeport
neighborhood. This unique styling boutique
for the "savvy & chic" has been in business for
the last three years and caters to women 21 and
older, sizes 0-3x, brides-to-be, and is also known to
dress up the girls and gents for prom season. Not limited
to selling classic and custom bridal gowns and accessories, the boutique rents
both dresses and tuxedos for the special day. Going beyond the call of styling,
staff rely upon their partnerships with designers and other bridal boutiques to
ensure the bride has her perfect dream dress and wedding party attire. Grab
your scheduler and visit this exclusive online salon which offers styling services
24/7. This store has since relocated to another city and state and will be opening
soon for in-store visitors.

Address| N/A
Phone| 701-404-9336
Hours| By Appointment only
Email| perfitbride@gmail.com
Price range| $$-$$$
Size range| All Sizes
Website| www.pmariebridalboutique.com
FB| PmarieBridal
IG| Pmariescb_stylist
First Time Shoppers Discount: Free Shop and style appointments for readers
and a **$5** rebate on online styling services.

Photo courtesy of Pamela Perkins

GLAM FASHION LOVE BOUTIQUE

Glam Fashion Love Boutique is a trendy, affordable fashion store located in the Southwest community of Brighton Park. This store keeps the fashion rolling with bargain deals that are to live for. Shop women's everyday wear,social attire, intimate apparel, shoes and accessories for under $100. You truly can get your money'sworth at this red and white decorated store symbolizing the fashion love that they offer. The owner Monique knows how to offer great products and customer service with a family history inentrepreneurship since her childhood days. There's no stopping the fashion, glam or love at this store.

Address| 5200 S. Archer Street , Suite 6 Chicago, IL 60632
Hours| Mon-Wed: 11am-6pm | Thurs-Sat: 11am-7pm
         Sun: Closed
Phone| 217-219-2440
Email| giflteamchicago@gmail.com
Price range| $-$$
Size range| S-3X | Special Order 4X-6X
Website| www.glamfashionlove.myshopify.com
FB| Glam Fashion Love
IG| Gfl_boutique
First Time Shopper's With Book | 5% In-store | use code LBBG online

A LOTTA GOOD STUFF UPSCALE
RESALE FURNITURE & MORE

ABSOLUTELY ANYTHING ESSENTIAL GIFT SHOP

BRONZEVILLE BOUTIQUE BY LADY MOCHA

FORTS SMITH BOUTIQUE ~ SPECIAL TRIBUTE

GOREE SHOP

A Lotta Good stuff Upscale Resale Furniture & More

This Bronzeville boutique is a treasure find in the neighborhood. This upscale resale boutique features everything from furniture, women's and men's apparel, to office equipment and the coolest vintage pieces you will find. The owner and current natural hair specialist, Benitta Phipps, has quickly become the new it girl. The store, birthed from her personal collection over the years, is quickly becoming a well sought out place to find highly-valued, unique one-of-a-kind pieces for both the home and wardrobe closet.

Address| 501 E.47th Street Chicago, IL 60653
Hours| Wed-Thurs:11am-6pm|Fri-Sat:10am-7pm|Sun-Tues:Closed
Phone| 708-724-3997
Email| Alottagoodstuff2@gmail.com
Price range| $$-$$$
Size range| N/A
FB| Alottagoodstuffupscale
IG| Alottagoodstuffoneofakindesign
First time shoppers discount| 20% in store

Absolutely Anything Essential Gift

Being nestled in Chicago's Bronzeville community for nearly four years now, Absolutely Anything Essential, LLC is a unique department store boutique-like hub of businesses coming together under one roof with something for everyone. From essential foods and dry goods ready to grab and the go to jewelry, body/ spa, home goods, natural hair products, souvenirs and cards --this boutique style market is the absolute go-to shop. Founded by Kenya Renee, originally as a pop-up gift shop with crafts and a recycled goods focus, the local staple has grown into its own incubator for local artists around the Windy City featuring works and products made by local and global brands. What's cool about the multi-level store is that guests can register for buy online and pick up in store options as well as choose Absolutely Anything Essential for the delivery of their WISH packages and upcoming Amazon locker location. Their online 'Do It Yourself' workshops are hosted in a variety of subjects including soap and fragrance making, painting, crafting, yoga, jewelry making and more! So, the next time you are in the area, swing by for a dose of Absolutely Anything Essential.

Address| 1915 W. 103rd Street Chicago, IL 60643
Hours| Mon-Fri:10am-6pm|Sat:10am-5pm|Sun:Closed
Phone|773-233-CHIC-2442
Email| info@belleup.com
Price Range| $$-$$$
Size Range| XS-3X
Website| www.BelleUp.com
FB|Belleupchicago| @belleupchicago
IG| Belleup
First Time Shoppers Discount With Book | N/A

Nearby Stores not featured in the this publication:

Remree's Bling's & Thing| located inside the Gift Shop
Website| www.remrees.com
First time shoppers discount| 20% off a Purchase $20 or more

Bronzeville Boutique by Lady Mocha

What can I say, Bronzeville Boutique has been one of Chicago's fashion go-to's in the Bronzeville community since 2009 and in business since 1991.Focusing on women's fashion, the store sits on the corner of the famous Martin Luther King Drive and 43rd Street just blocks away from one of Chicago's Home of Chicken and Waffles. For 20 years, the store's iconic fashionista alter ego, Lady Mocha, was created to symbolize the sexy, smart, and strong everyday women who shop the boutique. The store's clothing has been seen on the hit tv show Empire filmed in the Windy City and has been worn by many local celebrities. You can expect to find the latest edgy, trendy styles, accessories and knowledgeable in house fashion stylist.

Address| 4259 S. King Drive, Chicago, IL 60653
Hours| Mon–Sat:11am–7 pm|Sun:11am–5 pm
Phone| 773-891-4473
Email| Bronzevilleboutique@gmail.com
Price Range| $-$$$
Website| www.bronzevilleboutique.net/
FB| Bronzeville Boutique By Lady Mocha
IG| Boutiquebronzeville
First Time Shoppers Discount with Book| surprise instore discount|10%
online use code LBBG

Fort Smith Boutique ~ Special Tribute

This Bronzeville boutique was owned by one of Chicago's renowned jewelry designers, Mr. Clifford Smith, who passed away during the global COVID-19 Pandemic. With a fashion resume that includes designing jewelry for Spiegel and the famous Ebony Fashion Fair show, along with dressing famous singers such as Patti Labelle, Jennifer Holliday and Vanessa Bell Armstrong, his fashion craftsmanship and legacy will forever be remembered from his boutique stationed on 43rd Street. The glistening store featured a variety of handcrafted silver jewelry and custom feather masks. It's merchandise consisted of fine classic quality apparel and accessories for ladies ranging in ages from young working professionals to seasoned fashion divas. The owner and the store will forever hold a place in my heart. Let us remember Mr. Clifford Smith's many contributions to the fashion industry. May his legacy live on as one of Chicago's greatest jewelry designers.

Address| 1007 E. 43rd St, Chicago, IL 60653 - Permanently Closed
Hours| N/A
Phone| N/A
Email| N/A
Price range| $-$$$
Size range| sm-3x, Men's sportswear up to size 3X
FB| FortSmithBoutique | @ FortSmithBoutique
IG| Fort Smith Designer and Clothing Boutique
First Time Shoppers Discount With Book | N/A

Goree Shop

Named after the Goree island located off the coast of Dakar, Senegal. The owner strives to ensure that customers experience the authentic fashions of Africa as they step foot inside their doors surrounded with beautiful, vibrant colors of the motherland. The store features high quality African clothing at affordable prices. This store is great for both purchasing ready to wear African garments as well as fabrics. What's cool about this shop is that there is an in-store tailor ready to help give clients the best custom fit and designs of their choice. In addition to rich fabrics the store sells women's accessories, jewelry and spa products.

Address| 1122 E. 47th St, Chicago, IL 60653
Hours| Mon-Sat:10am-7pm|Sun:12pm-6pm
Phone| 773 285-1895
Email| adamaba190@gmail.com
Price Range| $-$$$
Size Range| All Sizes
Website| N/A
FB| Goree Shop
IG| adama190
First Time Shoppers Discount|10% instore

Nearby boutiques not featured in this publication:

Boutique Envie| 215 E. 47th ST, Chicago, IL 60653 | 773-633-2009
Legacy Men's Boutique| 4655 S. King Dr. Suite 103 Chicago, IL 60653 | 872-228-1871
www.legacymensboutique.com/
Pinke Junke Boutique| 3708 S. Indiana Ave, Chicago, IL | 773- 675-8431
www.pinkjunke.bigcartel.com/
Smartmove Furniture| 124 E. 51st ST, Chicago, IL | 773-855-2497
www.smartmovefurniture.com

BRIMS & ACCESSORIES

EFFORTLESS STYLE BOUTIQUE

ELLANA BOUTIQUE

ESSENTIAL ELEMENTS

KAYRA IMPORTS

LOOKS AND STYLE

MAXINE'S BOUTIQUE

ROSEBUD REFLECTIONS

Brims & Accessories

Brims is the place "Where Style Starts on Top" and is perfect for gentlemen seeking dapper headwear. Owned by Claude Wesley, Brims opened its doors in 2004 following the continued success of family owned men'swear shops on the South Side of Chicago. Brims is no ordinary hat shop. The shops serves as a sophisticated and heritage gatekeeper with inventory of Negro League Baseball caps and more. The store boasts hats, men's furnishings in a variety of styles, and brands ranging from Dobbs, Stetson, Bailey, Borsalino, Kangol, and more. If you've ever heard of the saying "A man isn't totally dressed up until he has a hat on..." --you can believe it, as this store has all the right styles to prove this saying to be true. Brims is certainly a destination hat-stop every fella must explore if they want to step out fully dressed up in a Brims kind of way.

Address| 1631 E. 87th Street, Chicago,IL 60617
Phone| 773-734-2820
Hours| Tues-Sat: 11am-6pm|Sun-Mon:Closed
Email| BrimsOfChicago@sbcglobal.net
Price range| $$-$$$
Size range| N/A
Website| www.brimsofchicago.com
FB| Brims & Accessories
IG| N/A
First Time Shoppers Discount with Book
10% instore |use code LBBG Online

Effortless Style Boutique

Style should be effortless, right? Well, that's the mission for this store located in the Avalon Park community. The owner Devonna's mission is to create an effortless shopping experience for men and women alike. In this boutique you can find a variety fashion must haves from denim, dresses, shoes & accessories, custom tees and more! Effortless Style Boutique also offers the latest deals on local events such as concerts and comedy shows happening around Chicago. If you're looking for casual pieces in white or denim, you're bound to find it here! Oh by the way, the store features a full pampering spa located in the rear of the store that specializes in manicures, pedicures, eyebrow waxing and eyelash extensions. How cool is that, a one stop shop done effortlessly.

Address| 424 E. 87th Street, Chicago, IL 60619
Hours| Tues-Sat 11am-7pm |Sun-Mon:Closed
Phone| 773-902-1900
Email| N/A
Price range| $-$$$
Size range| S-3X
Website| www.effortlessboutique.com/
FB| Effortless Boutique
IG| Effortless boutique
First time shoppers discount| 20% in store use code LBBG online

Essential Elements

For more than 30 years this family-owned upscale boutique has been a fashion jewel on the city's famous 87th Street near Stony Island. Surrounded by other Black-owned businesses, Essential Elements has proved to be a local favorite in the community with over 50 plus national and international designer brands for customers to choose from. Whether you're petite or full figured, this store has it all: apparel, jewelry, handbags, belts, hosiery, shoes, shoes, and more shoes! This fabulous boutique hosts annual fashion events that keeps the ladies coming back for more. This Boutique was once one of the exclusive homes to Miss Jessie's Natural Hair products.Taking a trip to this store is definitely worth the foot out the door and a step into style at Essential Elements!

Address| 1640 E. 87th Street, Chicago, IL 60617
Hours| Mon-Sat:11am -7pm|Sun:12pm-4pm
Phone| 773-978-1200
Email| eelements@sbcglobal.net
Price range| $-$$$
Website| www.shopeechicago.com
FB| Essential Elements-Chicago
IG| Essentialelementschicago
First time shoppers discount| 10% Instore | Use Code LBBG Online

Kayra Imports

What do you know about Kayra Imports? After my Kayra trail, I found that this chain of boutiques --all of which are located in Chicago's Hyde Park neighborhood on 83rd Street; and their largest location on 87th Street-- specializes in some of the best authentic African fashion attire and skin & body products from around the world. From Ghana, to Senegal, to Mali, and the Ivory Coast --they have it! The first store opened in 1983 and has since experienced longevity in the fashion-retail industry. Blown away by all of the African artifacts, soul traveling fashionistas could expect to fall in love with all of the things they can buy and take back home to their friends and family after a trip to Chicago. At Kayra Imports you can find incense, natural oils, soaps, drums, textile fabrics and more! Did I mention that they are the largest African online store? So you never have to leave your house when shopping with them. All I'm saying is go ahead and tell everyone you heard it from me.

Location#1
Address| 1643 E. 87th Street, Chicago, IL 60617
Phone| 773-768-3003
Hours| Mon-Sat: 10am-7pm
Location#2- Hydepark Community
Address| 1001 E.53rd Street, Chicago, IL 60615
Phone| 773- 363-5280
Hours| Mon-Sat:10am-7pm
Location#3- Chattam Community
Address| 706 E. 83rd Street, Chicago, IL 60619
Phone| 773-488-4123
Hours| Mon-Sat:10am -7 pm
Email| info@kayraimports.com
Price range| $-$$$
Size Range| All Sizes
Website| www.kayraimports.com
FB| KayraImports @ Kayraimports
IG| Kayra_Imports
First Time Shoppers Discount With Book | 10% in store use code LBBG online

Nearby Stores not featured in the this publication:

Sexy Hawt Clothing Store | 8202 S. Cottage Grove Chicago, IL 60619 | 725-212-6196
sexyhawtclothes.com

Looks and Style

At Looks and Style you can find all things Caribbean, from your favorite Bob Marley t-shirt to a host of cultural accessories and knick-knacks. This boutique is perfect for those traveling internationally and seeking out a dose of their homeland. The prices are amazing and the talented owner Crystal is a true multi-tasker and can recommend the perfect gift item to those who choose to grace her presence. Bring your coin pouch and get ready for fun, colorful fashion that will make you want to groove to your favorite Jamaican artist.

Address| 332 E 75th Street, Chicago, Illinois 60619
Phone| 872- 244-7397
Hours| Tues-Sat:11am-7pm|Sun:12pm-5pm
Email| N/A
Price range| $-$$$
Size range| All Sizes
Website| N/A
FB| Looks & Style Your Favorite Caribbean Store | @looksandstyleyou
IG| Looks & Style Your Favorite Caribbean Store
First Time Shoppers Discount With Book | 10% in store

Maxine's Boutique

For over 40 years Maxine's has been a pillar of fashion in the Avalon community. One of the oldest, thriving Black-owned fashion boutiques in all of Chicagoland, Maxine's Boutique continues to offer classy, sophisticated, fashion and accessories for women. The owner's daughter has carried on Ms. Maxine's legacy with a second location in Flossmoor, IL. As this family legacy lives on, so does the fashion as I was impressed with the owner's taste of style from shimmering evening accessories, shoes, and elegant dresses for any occasion. Something worth noting is that the store's shoes were annually featured during the 1970s-1980s for the iconic Ebony Fashion Fair, which was one of the world's largest traveling fashion shows produced by the late Eunice Johnson of the Johnson Publishing Company in Chicago.

Location#1
Address| 1613 E. 87th Street, Chicago, IL 60617
Phone| 773-221-8308
Hours| Mon-Fri:11am-7 pm Sat: 10am-7pm Sun: Closed
Email| shopmaxines@gmail.com
Price range| $$-$$$
Website| www.maxinesboutiques.com
FB| Maxine's Boutique | @MaxinesBoutiques
IG| maxinesboutiques
First time shoppers discount| 10% instore| use code LBBG online

Location#2 – Homewood ,IL
Address| 1938 Ridge Rd, Homewood, IL 60430
Phone| 708-922-9700 | 708- 922-9700
Hours| Tues-Sat:10:30am-6pm | Sun:Closed
Email| shopmaxines@gmail.com
Price range| $$-$$$
Website| www.maxinesboutiques.com
First time shoppers discount| 10% in store| use code LBBG online

Rosebud Reflections

Rosebud Reflections is a hidden fashion jewel located at the Cusp of Chicago's Great Grand Crossing & Chatham/Avalon neighborhood just a few doors away from popular black owned restaurants in the community. The owner Dora has been diligent in serving the surrounding communities with fun and affordable fashion for the last few years after relocating her store from its previous location for 5 years. The store is named after a nickname given to her by her dad as a child and is a reflection of her style and grace. It also serves as its own fashion incubator where other local artists and businesses can cultivate their products and blossom as entrepreneurs. You can find it all in this store from casual to chic to fabulous attire. The recently expanded store carries the latest trendy fashion, accessories, cosmetics, and hair & spa products. If you are looking for beautifully designed unique jewelry, this store has definitely got something for your fashion taste and budget.

Address| 1238-1240 East 79th Street, Chicago, IL 60619
Phone| 773-629-7726
Hours| Mon:12-4pm | Tue: By Appointment | Weds:12pm-6pm
         Thurs: Closed | Fri:12pm-6pm | Sat:11am-5pm
Price range| $-$$$
Email| dora@rosebudsreflections.com
Website| www.rosebudsreflections.com
FB| Rosebud's Reflections
IG| rosebudsreflections
First time shoppers discount| 10% instore

Nearby Stores not featured in the this publication:

Community Thrift Shop | 1244 E 79th st. Chicago, IL 60617| 773-437-4784

Ellana Boutique

Ellana Boutique, owned and operated by Ella for more than 20 years in the South Side's Chattam/Park Manor community, is a classic staple boutique with a relaxing luxurious atmosphere. With over 30 years of fashion experience, Ella is passionate about gaining new customers and retaining her loyal fashionista's since the turn of the early millennium. Ellana Boutique is a sophisticated store featuring some of the most elegant, classy attire for working and faith driven social women. From everyday wear to sassy formal outfits, the store houses the latest classic handbags and accessories. If you are looking for fancy church hats and attire this store is one of few that continues to help adorn our sistahs.

Address| 7511 S.Cottage Grove Ave Chicago, IL 60619
Hours| Wed-Sat: 10am -6pm| Sun:Closed
Phone| 773-846-8221
Email| ellanaboutique1@gmail.com
Price range| $$-$$$
Size range| XS-3X
Website| N/A
FB| Ellana Boutique | @ Ellana Boutique
IG| Ellanaboutique1
First Time Shoppers Discount With Book | 20% Instore

IRIDIUM BOUTIQUE

JERMIKKO DESIGN STUDIO

MOMADOU'S JEWELRY & CLOTHING

Iridium Boutique Co.

With two store locations inside the downtown Block 37 shopping mall and another location in Atlanta, this contemporary urban franchise store features some of the coolest fashion from both local and national brands including the store's own private label. Spearheaded by the founder Platinum in 2011, the biochemist turned celebrity stylist, along with the help of his partner Pugs, has created quite a buzz for the store attracting big names in entertainment such as Chris Brown and Justin Bibier. You can find both women's and men's apparel, accessories and shoes both in-store and online, as this store ships worldwide.

Location #1
Address| 108 N. State Street, First Floor, Chicago, IL 60602
Hours| Mon-Sat:11am-8pm | Sun:11am-6pm
Phone| 773-246-5488
Email| Thinkiridium@gmail.com
Price Range| $$-$$$
Size Range| S-2X
Website| www.iridiumclothingco.com/
FB| IridiumClothingCo | @iridiumClothing Co
IG| Iridiumclothingco
First Time Shopper's With Book| 10% in-store

Location #2
Iridium 77 Lab Downtown
Address| Block 37 Mall 2nd Floor, 108 N. State Street #232, Chicago, IL 60602
Hours| Mon-Sat: 11am-8pm | Sun: 11am-6pm
Phone| 312-775-2456
Email| thinkiridium@gmail.com
Price Range| $$-$$$
Size Range| S-2X
Website| www.iridiumclothingco.com/
FB| IridiumClothingCo | @iridiumClothing Co
IG| Iridiumclothingco
First Time Shopper's With Book| 10% in-store

Jermikko Design Studio and Production

Jermikko Shoshanna is the first African American to attend the School of the Art Institute and the University of Chicago, concurrently and the first woman owned, African American design and clothing manufacture in Illinois, Jermikko Shoshanna is no stranger to the fashion scene in Chicago. Since the late 70's her expansive career in fashion has continued to soar. From designing for other firms to starting her own firm with $50, she's well known for her innovative and timeless high-end fashion coats, suits, and evening wear under her Jermikko Label. Other labels such as the Possibles by Jermikko, fun wear and J by Jermikko, men'swear and SwapOut Hoodie Athleisure Wear- Mood by Jermikko are all current labels. Her clothing has been sold in major department stores such as Macy's and Saks, Nordstrom's, and in over 679 plus stores nationally and internationally. Jermikko has designed for movies and television series, as Spike Lee's Chi-Raq and Lee Daniels's Empire. Recently, one of her hoodies from her new sportswear line SwapOut Hoodie Athleisure Wear was seen worn in the "Lemonade" video by the superstar sensation, Beyoncé! Jermikko is listed in who's who in American Women, The HistoryMaker and The Library of Congress as a StyleMaker.

Address| 49 East Oak Street, 2nd floor, Chicago, IL 60611
Hours| Mon-Sat:11am- 5:30pm by appointment only
         and via online| Sun:Closed
Phone| 312-315-0760
Email| info@jermikko.com
Price range| Varies by Design $$-$$$$
Size range| All Sizes
Website| /www.jermikko.com| www.swapouthoodie.com
FB| jermikko
IG| Jermikkodesign
First Time Shoppers Discount With Book | N/A

MOMADOU'S JEWELRY & CLOTHING

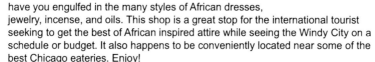

Centrally located in the James R. Thompson Center, this African Apparel & Accessories store is the perfect stop while in the downtown area. The owner of six years, Haje, caters to women from all around the world bolstering fashion and accessories from Mali, Senegal, Ghana and The Gambia. The store, a rainforest of vibrant colors, will have you engulfed in the many styles of African dresses, jewelry, incense, and oils. This shop is a great stop for the international tourist seeking to get the best of African inspired attire while seeing the Windy City on a schedule or budget. It also happens to be conveniently located near some of the best Chicago eateries. Enjoy!

Address| 100 . Randolph Street, Chicago, IL 60601 Unit 118
Phone| 773-407-2779
Hours| Mon-Fri: 8am -6pm | Sun:Closed
Email:| momadoudukurahm@yahoo.com
Price range| $-$$
Size range| All Sizes
Website:| www.theatriumchicago.com/
FB| Momadou's Jewelry & Clothing | @MomadousJewelryandClothing
IG| Momadousjewelry
First time shoppers discount| 10% Instore only

AGRICULTURE CUSTOM CLOTHIERS

MIAMI PARIS

Miami Paris

Yes, you read it right. The name of this trendy, chic women's only destination shop is Miami Paris, and just at one year's old. The store is owned by Nicole Williams whose professional background in project management prepared her to open her colorful shop in the Galewood neighborhood of the city's North westside. You can find casual to sophisticated looks in this boutique from everything including tops, bottoms, rompers, jumpsuits, cute dresses, coordinated ensembles, outerwear, swimwear and of course I can't forget the accessories. With junior, misses and plus sizes ranging from the small and petite to curvy figures, there's enough inventory for everyone. You don't have to travel thousands of miles to get the experience of high-quality fashion at your fingertips. Miami Paris promises to serve you with good fashion experience at an affordable price without jet setting across the country.

Address| 6812 W. North Avenue Chicago, IL 60707
Hours| Mon-Sat: 11am-7pm | Sun: 11am-4pm
Phone| 773-417-7994
Email| miamiparis1@gmail.com
Size Range| S-2X
Website| www.shopmiamiparis.com
FB| Miami Paris
IG| Miamiparisfashion
First Time Shoppers With Book| 15% in-store use code LBBG online

Agriculture Custom Clothiers

Agriculture Custom Clothiers is one of the best kept tailoring shops in the city. Owner Milton Latrell is best known for dressing the men of the town in the finest wardrobes to match their lifestyles. With a name like Agriculture, the motto rings true: "A Crop of Style." Grown like no other --this boutique, once located in the Bronzeville community, is an exclusive men's only store. With tailoring as a service, brothers are in for a treat at this upscale storefront that features casual, work, and social attire. Ladies can find the perfect gift for the special men in their life at this edgy boutique located in Chicago's Gold Coast community.

Address| 67 W. Chicago Ave, Chicago, IL 60654
Hours| Mon-Sat:11am-7pm | Sun:Closed
Phone| 312 877-5610
Email| agriculturecustomclothiers@gmail.com
Price range| $$-$$$$
Size range| S-4X
Website| www.shopagriculture.com/
FB| Agriculture AcropOfstyle
IG| Shopagriculture
First time shoppers discount| N/A

GILDA DESIGNER THRIFT BOUTIQUE   KILIMANJARO INTERNATIONAL

SILVER ROOM   SIR & MADAM

STAMP'LAYS EXECUTIVE SALON BOUTIQUE   WESLEY SHOES

GILDA Designer Thrift Boutique

GILDA Designer Thrift Boutique, named after the owner Gilda Norris, is a glistening fashion find in the Hyde Park Neighborhood. Having visited the area from Washington, DC and falling in love with the neighborhood, this is where she decided to mark her fashion territory. GILDA is an upscale, contemporary, vintage and resale shop full of exciting apparel and accessories for men and women all at an affordable price. You name it, they've got it --along with unique home decor and art. With years of experience in the fashion industry as a buyer, stylist, and merchandiser, Glida prides herself on offering quality merchandise and expert customer service. Opening their doors in 2016, the boutique has styled local and national celebrities such as jazz singer/radio personality D Alexander, along with the famous French sister duo Les Nubian, and former American Idol contestant Kiera Lanair from Chicago,IL.

Address| 1703 E. 55th Street, Chicago, IL 60637
Phone| 773- 888-3134
Hours| Tues12pm-7pm | Wed-Sat: 11am-7pm Sun: 12pm-5pm | Mon Closed
Email| Gilda.designerthriftboutique@gmail.com
Price range| $$-$$$
Size range| 0-24 (XS-2X)
Website| www.etsy.com/shop/GILDADesignerThrift
FB| GildaThrift Boutique
IG| Gilda.designerthriftboutique
First time shoppers discount| 10% instore | usecode LBBG online

Kilimanjaro International
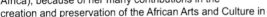

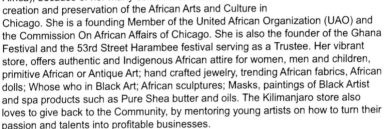

Named after the highest mountain in Africa located in Tanzania, East Africa. This Hyde park African Art & Cultural Design/,Gift Shop& Gallery store, has been the home away from the Motherland for Over 12 years. In fact, the owner is a native African., Affectionately nicknamed (Mama Africa), because of her many contributions in the creation and preservation of the African Arts and Culture in Chicago. She is a founding Member of the United African Organization (UAO) and the Commission On African Affairs of Chicago. She is also the founder of the Ghana Festival and the 53rd Street Harambee festival serving as a Trustee. Her vibrant store, offers authentic and Indigenous African attire for women, men and children, primitive African or Antique Art; hand crafted jewelry, trending African fabrics, African dolls; Whose who in Black Art; African sculptures; Masks, paintings of Black Artist and spa products such as Pure Shea butter and oils. The Kilimanjaro store also loves to give back to the Community, by mentoring young artists on how to turn their passion and talents into profitable businesses.

Address| 1305 E.53rd Street, Chicago, IL 60615
Phone| 773- 324-4860
Hours| Mon:2pm – 8pm | Tues-Sat:11am-7pm | Sun:12pm-5pm
Email| katumba2@live.com
Website| www.oneofakindafrica.com/
FB| Kilimanjaro International Inc.
IG| Kilimanjaro_chicago
First time shoppers discount| 10% in store

Silver Room

There hasn't been a retail experience quite like the Silver Room in Chicago since its birth in 1998. The 17-year-old business is a conglomerate mixture of community, culture, and art showcasing a variety of local and national artists in jewelry design, music and art. This local gathering place for all things artistic was inspired by owner Eric William's father who owned the Blue Room Bar. No matter the color of the room, you are bound to have a true authentic fashion experience with the silver room; just as the wife of celebrity actor Denzel Washington once did when she discovered the store on a trip to Chicago a few years back.

Address| 1506 E. 53rd Street. Chicago, IL 60615
Hour:| Mon-Sat 11am-8pm | Sun:11am-6pm
Phone| 773-947-0024
Email| info@thesilverroom.com
Price range| $-$$$$
Size range| XS-2X
Website| www.thesilverroom.com/
FB| Thesilverroom
IG| Thesilverroom
First Time Shoppers Discount|10% Instore|Use Code LBBG online

Sir & Madam

Owned by husband and wife Brian and Autumn Merritt, this online boutique is a unique shopper's experience for those who love casual, comfortable high-fashion urban wear. Formerly located in downtown Hyde park, quality fabrications serve as the backbone of this store's private label designs in men's and women's fashion/accessories. At this shop you can find everything from t-shirts, blazers, shirt jackets, bags and men's furnishings and shoes. This industrial vintage decorated store also collaborates with local designers to offer clients exclusive clothing brands in addition to classic staples that bring longevity to their customer's wardrobes.

Address| N/A
Hours| Mon-Sat:.11am–7pm|Sun: 12pm-5pm
Phone| 773-241-5225
Email| info@sirandmadame.com
Price range| $$-$$$
Size range| XS-2X
Website| www.sirandmadame.com/
FB| SirandMadameChicago
IG| Sir & Madam
First Time Shoppers Discount|N/A

Stamp'Lays Executive Salon Boutique

In a world where fashion is not all about the clothes, but what you showcase from your head to your toes, Stamp'Lays is just that. The hairstylist, salon and boutique owner Kimberly Stampley has combined two things she loves into one unique experience: fashion and hair. For more than seventeen years this unique store features some of the most exclusive fashion apparel around town that will have you envisioning yourself as an executive. The bold, sparkling, glitzy jewelry, and fur trimming dresses are bound to have corporate sistahs rushing from the plane to her executive salon where they can really get styled from head to toe. Located in the heart of Hyde Park on 53rd Street, this boutique reflects the surrounding scenery of fashion with dozens of little shops along the strip to make your trip to her shop worth the while. Serving sizes 0-3X

Address| 1371 E. 53rd Street, Chicago, IL 60615
Hours| Tues-Fri:10am–7pm | Sat:7am–7pm Sun- Mon: Closed
Phone| 773-241-6200
Email| KimberlyStamplay@gmail.com
Price range| $$-$$$
Size range| 0-3X
Website| N/A
FB| Stamp'Lays
IG| Stamp'Lays
First Time Shoppers Discount With Book| 20% instore

KAYRA IMPORTS LOCATION #2 | see pg33

Nearby stores not featured in this publication:

Shop 500 Boutique| 5847 S. State St Chicago, IL 60621|773-643-9393
www.shop500boutique.com
The Silver Umbrella| 5305 S. Hyde Park Blvd,Chicago, Illinois 60615| 773- 675-6114
www.thesilverumbrella.com/

Wesley Shoes

Wesley Shoes has boasted longevity since 1970 and is the oldest ongoing African American owned shoe store in the USA. The year 2020 marks their 50th year in business and in 2019 Wesley's was voted by the Industry and Footwear Insights as the #1 independent retailer in Illinois and 13th in the USA! "The Five-Star Treatment" has been the motto for Wesley Shoes since its existence and offers customized services such as using the latest technology to measure the feet of customers to ensure the best fit possible. Located in Hyde Park, the owner Bruce Wesley has served Chicagoan families including the late John Johnson of Ebony Magazine, Civil Rights leader John Lewis, and Barack Obama, the first Blzack president of the United States of America.

Address| 1506 E. 55th Street, Chicago, IL 60615
Hours| Mon-Fri: 9:30am-7pm | Sat: 9:30am-6pm | Sun: 12pm-5pm
Phone| 773-667-7463
Email| wesleyshoes@aol.com
Price range| $$_$$$
Website| www.wesleyshoes.com
FB| Wesley Shoes | @Wesleyshoes
IG| Wesleys.Shoes
First Time Shoppers Discount With Book | N/A

Nearby stores not featured in this publication:

Shop 500 Boutique| 5847 S. State St Chicago, IL 60621|773-643-9393
www.shop500boutique.com
The Silver Umbrella| 5305 S. Hyde Park Blvd,Chicago, Illinois 60615| 773- 675-6114
www.thesilverumbrella.com/

STYLE ROOM 326

Style Room 326

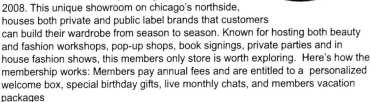

Style Room 326 is just that: Chicago's first members only wholesale and retail showroom. Owned by Teresa Washington, a woman with extensive experience when it comes to owning, operating and traveling for her fashion retail businesses and nonprofit organizations since 2008. This unique showroom on chicago's northside, houses both private and public label brands that customers can build their wardrobe from season to season. Known for hosting both beauty and fashion workshops, pop-up shops, book signings, private parties and in house fashion shows, this members only store is worth exploring. Here's how the membership works: Members pay annual fees and are entitled to a personalized welcome box, special birthday gifts, live monthly chats, and members vacation packages

Address| 1722 W. Belmont Ave, Chicago ,IL 60657
Hours| Wholesale Buyers Mon-Tues:By appointment only.Open to the Public
　　　　Thurs:11am-8pm Online Hrs | Mon-Fri:9:30am-6pm | Sat-Sun:9:30am-5pm
Phone| 855-727-4751
Email| info@styleroom326.com
Price range| $$-$$$
Size Range XS-XL
Website| www.styleroom326.com/
FB| Styleroom326
IG| _styleroom326
First time shoppers discount| 15% discount shipping on a total purchase of $100

Near by boutiques not featured in this publication:

Uptown| African Wonderland Imports | 4423 N.Broadway Street, Chicago, IL 60640|773- 334-2293
Afrikiko Hair and Fashion Boutique | 4659 N. Broadway St. Chicago, IL 60640 | 773 8784360

EdgeWater Community
African Safari Imports| 1140 W.Bryn Mawr Ave Chicago, IL 60660| 773- 549-2744
　　　　　　www.africansafariimports.com/

Rogers Park
Creme De la Creme Resale shop| 1352 W. Devon Ave, Chicago, IL 60660 872-208-5089
Lady B. Boutique| 1547 N. Howard St Chicago, IL 60623 | 312-714-2485
Lakeside Treasures |1520 W. Jarvis Ave Chicago, IL 60626 | 773- 262-9354
M Dramain| 1424 W Morse Ave Chicago IL 60626 | 773-856-0995
Unan Imports| 6971 N.Sheridan Rd Chicago, IL 60626 | 773- 274-4022

CUSTOM BY LAMAR

KIWIS BOUTIQUE

SOLE' RESALE BOUTIQUE

Custom by Lamar

Custom by Lamar, is a destination designer studio owned and operated by Celebrity Fashion Designer, Lamar Giles for over 22yrs. The business specializes in creating unique one of kind clothing for women, men and kids. From Prom attire, sportswear and extravagant apparel, clothing is designed with the customer in mind from start to finish. Lamar a chicago native, who fell in love with fashion design as a kid, returned to that passion utilizing both his bachelors and master degrees he obtained in the areas of business and finance from Huston-Tillotson University 93 and Roosevelt University in 93.to lead along side his star team of master tailors operating the business. Lamar has had the luxury of boasting current celebrity clients such as Shaquilled Oneal whom he outfitted for the basketball stars wedding along with his entire groomsmen, to big names such Michael Jordan, Dwayne Wade, Honorable Minister Louis Farrakhan, Judge Mathis,Secretary of State Jesse White and last but not least even Oprah has graced Custom by Lamar, how fabulous is that?This exclusive design Studio is the go toplace for all things custom with sample items display daily to choose from for all your custom needs.

Address| 2423 W. Madison Street, Chicago, Illinois 60612
Hours| Tues-Fri: 11am-6pm | Sat:12pm-5pm | Sun-Mon: Closed
Phone| 312-738-2160
Email| custombylamarinc@yahoo.com
Prize Range | $$$-$$$$$
Size range| All Sizes
Website| N/A
FB| Custom by Lamar Inc.
IG| Custombylamarinc
First time shoppers discount| 10% in store

Kiwis Boutique

This bright and colorful 15 years old boutique in orange and lime green is bound to catch the eye of any fashionista. The husband and wife owners know how to make any couple stand out in a crowd. With both men's and women's social attire, the store offers the best of both worlds. Shoppers of all figures and sizes can enjoy the array of colorful fashion in store from jewelry, handbags, and home goods consisting of room sprays, candles and more. One of the best parts about the store is the comfy sofa decorated in their signature colors as they make Chicagoans feel right at home while shopping in their store closet.

Address| 1015 S. Western Ave. Chicago, IL 60612
Hours| Weds–Sat: 11am-7pm | Sun-Tues: Closed
Phone: 312-421-3322
Email| info@kiwisboutiqueinc.com
Price range| $-$$$
Size range| Women: XS-3X | Men's Size: 32-38
Website| www.kiwisboutiqueinc.com/
FB| Kiwis Boutique
IG| kiwisboutique | @ kiwisboutique
First Time Shoppers Discount With Book| 15% instore| use code LBBG online

Near by boutiques not featured in this publication:

Fashionably Unpredictable| 1017 S.Western Ave. Chicago, IL 60612 | 312- 701-4214
www.fashionablyunpredictable.com/

Sole' Resale Boutique

Social humanitarianism is the focus behind this resale shop located right outside of the downtown area. The owner, Natasha Rolling, thrives on providing the community with upscale new and gently worn clothing. Sole Resale Boutique offers consignment and accepts donations regularly from consumers who see the value in giving back. This is the store for those who are budget conscious and love all things vintage, classic and genuine. Living up to their sassy tagline "Look great and don't break the bank for fashion."

Address| 2413 W. Madison Street,Chicago IL ,60612
Hours| Tues-Sat: 9:30am-6pm|Sun-Mon: Closed
Phone| 312- 637-9699
Email| soleresaleboutique@yahoo.com
Price range| $-$$$
Size range| Men's & Women:XS-4X/5X
Website| www.soleresale.com
FB| Soleresaleboutique
IG| Soleresaleboutique
First Time Shoppers Discount With Book | 10% Instore

Near by boutiques not featured in this publication:

Leaders 1354| 152 W Madison St, Chicago, IL 60607 | Call 312- 787-7144
www.ldrs1354.com/
Personal Privelage| 1442 N Milwaukee Ave, Chicago, IL 60622| 773- 235-6090
www.personalprivilege.com/

SHERNETT SWABY

Shernett Swaby

Jamaican born designer, Shernet Swaby, is a high-fashion favorite in Chicago and former finalist on the hit television show, Project Runway. She is the edgy-chic artist serving the Chicagoland area the last 10 years both in the Wicker Park and Ukrainian Village neighborhoods before moving her store to its current location in River North. It's also worth noting that her 20 years plus flagship store located in Toronto, Canada has stood the test of time. Clothing in her boutique breaks all of the fashion rules with styles that rebel against fast fashion trends of the moment and caters to women of all shapes and sizes with the designer's avant-garde looks. The designer creates long lasting fashion, often stitched by her, and offers all clients free Alterations throughout the life cycle of her garments. The diverse women who shop the designer's architectural aesthetics come from all age groups, but often range from age 30-65. The store assortments include responsibly made apparel along with leather accessories and handbags.

Location# 1
Address| 750 N. Franklin Street Chicago, IL 60654
Hours| Tues- Sat:10am-6pm | Sun-Mon: Closed:
Phone| 312-533-1745
Email| shernettswaby@gmail.com
Price range| $$-$$$
Size range| All Sizes
Website| www.shernettswaby.com
FB| swaby_rebel
IG| swaby_rebel

Location # 2 Canada
Address| 632 Queen Street W. Toronto, ON M6J 1E4, Canada
Hours| Tues-Sat:11am-7pm cst | Sun-Mon: Closed
Phone| 416-203-6860
Email| shernettswaby@gmail.com
Website| www.shernettswaby.com
FB| Swaby_rebel
IG| Swaby_rebel
First Time Shoppers Discount With Book| schedule an appointment and use code: BOB19 to receive $100 off on your first purchase at SWABY

BARBARA BATES DESIGNS

MS. CATWALK

SUCCEZZ

Barbara Bates Designs

Barbara Bates Designs is a name worth knowing in the Chicagoland area for exclusive, unique custom wear created by none other than Ms. Bates herself. More than just a designer, the breast cancer survivor wows the city every year with her annual "Knocking Out Breast Cancer" charity fashion shows featuring both local and national celebrity clients for the last 25 years . If you're in town and you want to connect with an upscale boutique driven on offering quality, lavish high fashion since 1987, then this is the place to set up your appointment to create something magical for decades to come. What's cool is that customers can shop the designer's custom pieces as well as her newly launched retail selections in apparel and outerwear.

Address| 2031 S. Indiana Ave, Chicago, IL 60616
Hours| Mon-Fri:9am-5pm | Sat:By appointment Sun:Closed
Phone| 312-808-8091
Email| info@barbarabatesdesigns.com
Website| www.barbarabatesdesigns.com
Price range| Varies by Design $$$-$$$$
Size range| All Sizes
FB| Barbarabatesdesigns
IG| Barbara_bates
First time shoppers discount| 10% off Instore

Ms. Catwalk

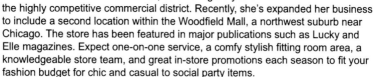

Owned by private attorney and juvenile probation officer Michon Stuttley for over 10 years, Ms. Catwalk's flagship store stands alone in the South Loop for offering affordable chic clothing for women in both misses to plus sizes. Her style from the courtroom and as a private attorney specializing in intellectual properties to fashion is serious business for her, celebrating six years in the highly competitive commercial district. Recently, she's expanded her business to include a second location within the Woodfield Mall, a northwest suburb near Chicago. The store has been featured in major publications such as Lucky and Elle magazines. Expect one-on-one service, a comfy stylish fitting room area, a knowledgeable store team, and great in-store promotions each season to fit your fashion budget for chic and casual to social party items.

Location #1
Address| 2311 S. Michigan Ave Chicago, IL 60616
Hours| Tues-Sat:11am-7pm | Closed Sun-Mon
Phone| 312-929-3360
Email| mscatwalkboutique@gmail.com
Price range| $-$$$
Size range| XS-3X
Website| www.mscatwalk.com/
FB| Ms. Catwalk | @mscatwalkboutique
IG| mscatwalkboutique
First time shoppers discount| 15% instore | use code LBBG online

Location #2
Woodfield Mall 2nd Floor
Address| 5 Woodfield Mall, Schaumburg, IL 60173-5097 2nd flr,
Hours| please see mall hrs @ www.simon.com/mall/woodfield-mall
Phone| 224-520-8488
Email| mscatwalkboutique@gmail.com
Website| www.mscatwalk.com/
FB| Ms.Catwalk | @mscatwalkboutique
IG| Mscatwalkboutique
First time shoppers discount| 15% instore | use code LBBG online

Succezz

At this South Loop store, it's all about the gym shoes and other sporty athletic fashions for him and for her. Owned by former NBA players Bobby Simmons and LaVelle VDOT Sykes, the shop offers some of the best sportswear for men and women. From national brands such as Nike, Jordan, and other sporty brands, visitors can expect real, authentic footwear like no other. With its frequent sidewalk sales and knowledgeable store staff, the store is a hub for the sports lovers looking for the fresh comfortable clothing.

Address| 2214 S. Michigan Ave, Chicago, IL 60616
Hours| Mon-Sat: 10am- 8pm | Sun:11 am-4pm
Phone| 312-431-1900
Email| succezz1329@gmail.com
Price Range| $$-$$$
Website| www.succezzthestore.com/
FB| SuccezZ
IG| succezzthestore
First Time Shoppers Discount with Book| 10% instore Use code LBBG online
*Store Hrs May Vary By Season

Near by boutiques not featured in this publication:

Annies Accents| 1237 S. Michigan Ave, Chicago, IL 60605 | Call 312- 588-0496
www.aniesaccents.com/
Kido| 1137 S. Delano Ct.Chicago, Illinois 60605| 312-285-2957
www.kidochicago.com/

PERFECT PIECES

SULLIVAN FASHIONS (LEGACY BOUTIQUE)

Perfect Pieces

Perfect Pieces is a boutique located in the South Shore community of Chicago. The store caters to stylish women looking for the right piece to complment their wardrobe and lifestyle. The owner not only places an emphasis on clothing, but on the right piece of jewelry to accentuate the overall outfit. Perfect Pieces is a spinoff of their hair extensions boutique and promises its customers to be the perfect place for chic and social attire for women of a various sizes ranging from small to large.

Address| 7207 S. Exchange Ave, Chicago, Illinois 60649
Hours| Tues-Fri:10am-6pm | Sat:10am-7:30pm | Sun: Closed
Phone| 872-225-2117
Email| ms.camara@yahoo.com
Price range| $-$$$
Size range| Small-3X
Website| www.perfectpiecesboutique.com
FB| Perfect Pieces
IG| Perfect_pieces2
First Time Shoppers Discount With Book | 10% instore

Near by boutiques not featured in this publication:

Zion Wellness Center | 7209 S. Exchange Ave, Chicago, IL 60649|773- 819-0894

Sullivan Fashions (Legacy Boutique)

Sullivan Fashions is owned and operated by
Mr. Sullivan and his wife for over 51 years. This
high fashion store caters to career and social
savvy women. The store hosts exclusive catalog
selections from outerwear, dresses and suits of
some of the most recognized brands such as Donni
Vinci. This luxury store is not only a historical jewel
in its community, it is a source of hope and inspiration to
aspiring fashion retail owners who seek quality merchandise that will surely stand
the test of time. As a master Tailor, Mr. Sullivan has had the pleasure of suiting up
some of the best local officials, executives and faith based women from all over
the city; proving that his business is a treasure to be found!

Address| 2524 E. 75th Street, Chicago, IL 60649
Hours| Tues-Sat:11am-6pm | Sun-Mon: Closed
Phone| 773-731-2122
Email| N/A
Price range| $-$$$
Size range| 10-24, special order sizes available above size 24
FB| Sullivan's Fashions
IG| N/A
First Time Shoppers Discount with Book | N/A Customers receive 10-20% daily year
round

Nearby Stores Not Featured in This Publication:

Z Couture| 9242 S. Stony Island Chicago, IL | 708-261-1638
http://www.zcouturechicago.com

BORRIS POWELL STUDIOS

SARAH KUENYEFU

Borris Powell Studios

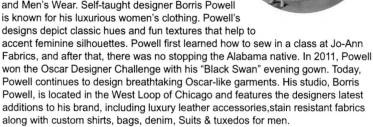

Borris Powell Designs is truly a luxury men's and women's Oscars red carpet brand. The Borris Powell studio is located in West Town / Humboldt Park and features the designer's latest addition to the brand: luxury leather accessories and Men's Wear. Self-taught designer Borris Powell is known for his luxurious women's clothing. Powell's designs depict classic hues and fun textures that help to accent feminine silhouettes. Powell first learned how to sew in a class at Jo-Ann Fabrics, and after that, there was no stopping the Alabama native. In 2011, Powell won the Oscar Designer Challenge with his "Black Swan" evening gown. Today, Powell continues to design breathtaking Oscar-like garments. His studio, Borris Powell, is located in the West Loop of Chicago and features the designers latest additions to his brand, including luxury leather accessories,stain resistant fabrics along with custom shirts, bags, denim, Suits & tuxedos for men.

Address| 1633 N. Hamlin Ave. Suite 201, Chicago, IL 60661
Hours| Tues-Sat:12pm-7pm and By appointment
Phone| 773- 857-5585
Email| bpowell@borrispowell.com
Price range| Varies by design $$-$$$$
Size Ranges | XS-XL | Custom Designs Available
Website| www.borrispowell.com/
FB| Borrisjpowell | @BorrisPowell
IG| Borrispowelldesigns
First Time Shoppers Discount With Book | 20% off RTW 10% off Custom in store

Sarah Kuenyefu

Launched in 1991, the Sarah Kuenyefu collection is named after the Ghanian born designer located on 63rd street in the Woodlawn community of Chicago. The store stocks a wide variety of her classically elegant designs that are timeless, comfortable, functional and stylish all in one. Inspired by both her African heritage and Western silhouettes, the designer focuses on creating looks that flatter her customers' unique body features. Amongst the designer's own private label, shoppers can find stylish jewelry and accessories, including hosiery and spa products.

Address| 1510 E. 63rd Street, Chicago, IL 60637
Hours| Mon-Sat: 11am-7pm | Sun: Closed
Phone| 773-324-6858
Email| info@sarahkuenyefu.com
Price range| $-$$$
Size range| XS-3X | Custom Designs Available
Website| www.sarahkuenyefu.com
FB| Sarahkuenyefucollection | @sarahkuenyefucollection
IG| Sarahkuenyefu
First Time Shoppers Discount With Book| 10% instore | use code LBBG online

Annie Bell Fragrances

If you are looking for more than a little aromatherapy? Then this smell good brand could be your next favorite item to sniff and buy across Chicago. Formerly located on the border of Chicago's West Side and Oak Park, IL, Annie Bell Fragrances contains an assortment of over ten handmade smell good and feel good products ranging from soy candles, natural soaps, body butters, and essential oils. All products are 100% natural and Fallon Johnson is simmering up the right scents with her brand. Named after the owner's late grandmother, the fragrance brand is an all smell good, feel good product to shop for yourself or gift to others.

Select WholeFood Markets(Chicagoland Area)

Address| PO Box 4595, Chicago, IL. 60680
Hours| www.wholefoodsmarket.com/stores
   www.anniebellfragrances.com/new-page
Phone| 1-888-781-1249
Email| info@anniebellfragrances.com
Price range| $- $$
Website| www.anniebellfragrances.com/
FB| Anniebellfragrances
IG| anniebellfragrances
First time shoppers discount| N/A

CLASSY CLOSET CONSIGNMENT BOUTIQUE

GET EYED BOUTIQUE

STEPPING OUT ON FAITH CONSIGNMENT SHOP

Classy Closet Consignment Boutique

For the past 16 years, Mr. Wilder has turned his multi-level consignment boutique into one of "Chicago's Premier Source for Luxury Consignment" for both women and men making his store motto a reality. With well-known designer brands and a large selection of merchandise offerings from clothing, shoes, bags and accessories, jewelry, vintage and antique items, it's no surprise that this shop has frequent visitors from both Chicago and other states. From gently worn to new merchandise at affordable pricing, this store has become a staple for both the young and the mature within Evanston and the surrounding communities.

Address| 701 Washington, Evanston, IL 60202
Phone| 1-847-475-0355
Hours| Mon- Sat:10am-6pm | Sat: 10am-5pm | Sun:12pm-5pm
Email| shopclassycloset@gmail.com
Price range| $-$$$$
Website| www.classyclosetconsignment.com
FB| Classy Closet Consignment
IG| Shopclassyclosetconsignment

Get Eyed Boutique

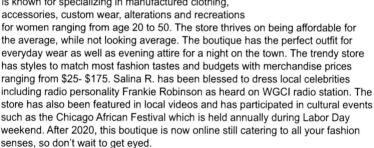

Get Eyed Boutique Is chic little boutique located in Evanston, IL founded by Salina R. in 2013. The owner's eye for fashion has followed her throughout her fashion journey, first as a child observing her mom's wardrobe, and later during her career as a stylist. The boutique is known for specializing in manufactured clothing, accessories, custom wear, alterations and recreations for women ranging from age 20 to 50. The store thrives on being affordable for the average, while not looking average. The boutique has the perfect outfit for everyday wear as well as evening attire for a night on the town. The trendy store has styles to match most fashion tastes and budgets with merchandise prices ranging from $25- $175. Salina R. has been blessed to dress local celebrities including radio personality Frankie Robinson as heard on WGCI radio station. The store has also been featured in local videos and has participated in cultural events such as the Chicago African Festival which is held annually during Labor Day weekend. After 2020, this boutique is now online still catering to all your fashion senses, so don't wait to get eyed.

Address| Online
Hours| Tues-Fri:11:30am-7pm | Sat:11am-7:30pm
Phone| 847-425-0030
Email| geteyed@yahoo.com
Size range| S-3X (2-20)
Website| www.Geteyed.com
FB| Eye Boutique Kloset
IG| Geteyed
First Time Shoppers Discount With Book| 15% online use code LBBG

Stepping Out on Faith Consignment Shop

Established in 2009 in Chicago's Evanston suburb, this store offers some of the best gently worn and vintage clothing, shoes and accessories for both men and women around town. After the loss of her husband, owner Vivian Killebrew promised him that she would step out on faith and open her fashion store as he wanted her to do. Well, fast forward with 11 years of business behind her fashion belt, she's fulfilling her dream. With well known designer brands such as Eilleen Fisher, Coach, St. John, Joan of New York and more in store, fashionistas are bound to be blessed with affordable, chic treasure finds for their closets. Not only is she a blessing to her clients, Ms. Killebrew found a way to serve her community by partnering with a popular organization "Connection for the Homeless," which provides homeless prevention, shelter and housing to over thirty-eight north suburban communities.

Address| 1632 Orrington Ave, Evanston, IL 60201
Hours| Tues-Sat:11am-6pm | Sun: Closed
Phone| 847-733-0980
Email| viviank570@yahoo.com
Price range| $-$$$$
Size range| Women's:0-28 | Men's Jackets: 34-60 Pants: 28-50
Website| www.steppingoutonfaith.com
FB| Stepping Out On Faith1632
IG| Steppingoutonfaithconsignment
First time shoppers discount| 20% instore

Near by boutiques not featured in this publication:

Minouchic Boutique| 1900 Asbury Ave ste b, Evanston, IL 60201| 847-859-2066

ANJEL'S BOUTIQUE

DIVINE SOLE BOUTIQUE

TERESA FE FE DESIGNS

WIRED BY DESIGN BOUTIQUE

Anjel's Boutique

Since 2013, Anjel's Boutique founder and owner Towanna Walker (Butler) has mastered the local fashion industry serving the south suburbanland fashionista;s of Chicago. The name of this trendy store was inspired from the owner's Father,who gave his daughters the nickname "Jeff's Angels" . The Sentimental Name honor;s her father legacy and with the support of her family, the boutique has been flourishing with business, driven on helping women develop their personal styles through clothing that strengthen their confidence. The store caters to women of various sizes from small to full-figured. Shoppers can expect to find stylish clothing, outerwear, handbags, jewelry, and a small selection of shoes for both women and men when visiting the store or shopping online.

Address| 18050 Dixie Hwy, Homewood, IL 60430
Hours| Tues-Fri:11am-7pm | Sat:11am-6:30pm
Phone| 708-799-7419
Email| anjels_boutique@sbcglobal.net
Price range| $$-$$$
Size range| XS-3X
Website| www.anjelsboutique.com
FB| AnjelsBoutique | @AnjelsBoutique
IG| anjelsboutique
First Time Shoppers Discount With Book | 10% instore| Use code LBBG online

MAXINE'S BOUTIQUE LOCATION #2 | see pg35

Near by boutiques not featured in this publication:
Mystique Boutique| 18123 Dixie Hwy, Homewood, IL 60430| 708-922-9560

Wired The **Design**
BOUTIQUE

Womens, Plus & Kids Clothing

www.wiredthedesignboutique.com

Photo Credit: Michael Sundjata Johnson
Models: Tonya Byrd Neeley
Charlotte Walker
Kennedi Neeley
Kenzi Neeley

Wired The Design Boutique

Wired The Design Boutique is a new boutique on the block having just opened within the last few years. Tonya Byrd-Neeley is the owner of this new store located in Flossmoor, IL. With a B.S. in Business Management from Grambling State University and as a previous specialty store manager for corporate store names such as Express, Foot Locker, Ulta, and Fossil, Tanya knows how to offer her customers a great shopping experience and thrives on making them feel both unique and special. Hince the store's motto "Fashion You Can Buy, But Style You Possess." At this boutique, you can find women's trendy, contemporary, business, and outerwear in a variety of sizes up to 3x. That's not all --they also carry a selection of men'swear including jeans, cargo pants, t-shirts, and general sportswear. The store's clientele is fit for energetic teenagers along with their mature edgy grandma's. There's no age limit to the style in this store. The store is expected to launch a private label for both full-figured men and women in the near future. There's no reason not to get wired by all the cool fashion in this store.

Address| 1056 Sterling Flossmoor, IL 60422 Unit 12
Hours| Mon-Thurs:10am-6pm | Sat:10am-7pm | Sun:11am-4pm By appointment
Phone| 708-799-5601
Email| wiredthedesignboutique@gmail.com
Price range| $-$$$
Size range| XS-3X
Website| www.wiredthedesignboutique.com/
FB| Wired | The Design Boutique LLC | @Wiretdb
IG| wiredtdb
First Time Shoppers Discount With Boutique

Divine Sole Boutique

Divine Soul Boutique carries a variety of fashion merchandise from women's apparel, shoes, and accessories, online and instore. A native of Chicago, Sabrina Davis has years of experience in fashion with a family background and education in business that reflects her previous store's success for over ten years in Homewood, IL. This online boutique, known for its superior customer service, cool incentives, annual fashion shows, in-store stylists, fashion parties, and stellar online customer support --has won over the South Chicagoland suburbs. Don't believe me? Visit the website for yourself at www.divinesoulboutique.com and shop these chic, affordable fashions.

Address| Online
Hours| Online
Phone| 708 336-3601
Email| info@divinesoleboutique.com
Price range| $-$$$
Size range| XS-3X
Website| www.divinesoleboutique.com/
FB| Divine Sole Boutique | @Divine Sole Boutique
IG| divinesoleboutique
First Time Shoppers Discount With Book | 10% online only. Use code LBBG

Teresa Fe Fe Designs

Celebrity artist and designer Teresa Fe-Fe
Barrow is the driving force behind Teresa
Fe-Fe Designs. Ms. Fe-Fe's uniquely created
designs consist of hand-painted jackets, purses,
hats, shoes, and wall art. Her unique creativity
has landed her in numerous magazines, videos,
plays and runway shows with her designs being seen
internationally. Ms. Fe-Fe has designed for Glenn Jones,
Mike Epps, members of the music group Lakeside and Con Funk Shun, with the
bass player as one of her celebrity brand ambassadors. She has positioned herself
with being highly sought after by many performing artists for unique stage designs.
To date, one of her main accomplishments is opening her own art and fashion
design studio for men and women in Crete, IL.

Address| 565 W. Exchange Crete, IL 60417
Hours| By appointment
Phone| 708-623-3326
Email| teresabarrow4@hotmail.com
Price range| $$-$$$
Size range| All sizes | custom designs available
Website| N/A
FB| TERESAFEFEDESIGNS
IG| Teresa Fe-Fe Designs
First Time Shoppers Discount With Book | 10% instore

AVANT GARDE BOUTIQUE

CHIC CHICK'S BOUTIQUE

HYFALUTEN BOUTIQE

LADIES AND GENTLEMEN BOUTIQUE

LET'S DO IT AGAIN RESALE BOUTIQUE

LURE BOUTIQUE

PERFECT FIT FASHIONS & ACCESSORIES

PURSENALATIES HANDBAGS & JEWELRY

SUIT PLUS MORE

TAJ B COUTURE "FASHION HOUSE"

THE LADIES CONSIGNMENT BOUTIQUE

Hyfaluten Boutiqe

As one of the first Black boutiques to open in Berywn, IL, this captivating shop is breaking all the fashion rules with its big, bold and colorful fashion assortment. The owner Natasha Hall's dream of manifesting her 10 year old fashion business into a brick and mortar recently became a reality. The transportation industry professional turned fashionista coined her store name "Hyfalutin with an "E" from a series of popular phrases used by the late great poet Maya Angelou, To describe something that is over the top & fancy. Stepping into this bright and beautifully decorated store is like taking a trip on a fashion fairy tale. The clothing speaks for itself as each garment and accessory is a conversation to be had. The store features trendy, chic and elegant clothing, accessories, shoes, spa and fragrances for women. They also provide private shopping parties and event space for women looking to host small intimate gatherings with like-minded fashionistas. If you are looking to make a bold statement at your next party or event —don't worry, because the fashion here is too fancy not to be seen!

Address| 6303 W. Roosevelt Road, Berwyn, IL 60402
Phone| 708- 663-0348
Hours| Tues-Fri: 11:30am-7pm Sat: 11:30am-7:30pm Sun-Mon: Closed
Price range| $$-$$$
Email| Hyfaluten@gmail.com
Website| www.hyfaluten.website/
FB| Hyfaluten
IG| hyfaluten
First time shoppers discount| 10% instore only

Avant Garde Boutique

Located in downtown Forest Park, IL, this uber high fashion boutique is part of the crème de la crème of the fashion crop. Formerly known by the name of Sassy Couture for the last five years, fashion extraordinaire Patricia A. McMillan is no stranger to the fashion industry having previously owned a popular store in the Chatham neighborhood ten years prior to relocating her store to the West suburbs. Since then, it has metamorphosed into the whimsical Avant Garde store it is today. With the addition of its new store partner Katrina GoldWebb, a US Navy veteran, the new store pays tribute to its former legacy by offering some of the best cutting edge international designer brands for high society conscious fashionistas. When visiting this store be prepared to experience the beautiful Parisian inspired decor infused with fierce red and leopard printed wall accents, followed by exceptional fashion forward designs and customer service. Women can expect to shop from a variety of exclusive fashions for fun social gatherings to elegant formal events. With monthly in-store shopping and networking events --you're bound to make new friends and support the many social charity fundraisers initiatives the store supports including breast cancer survivor events. Finally, if you are looking to host your own girl's night out with your favorite BFF's --then they've got the fashion and the space!

Address| 7601 W. Madison Street,Ste. D, Forest Park, IL 60130
Hours| M-F By Appointment Only | Sat:10am-6pm | Sun:11am-4pm
Phone| 708- 252-9072 | 708-698-0418
Email| katrina@theavantgardeboutique.com
Size range| S-3X (0-24)
Website| www.theavantgardeboutique.com/
FB| Avant Garde Boutique
IG| The.Avant.Garde.Boutique
First Time Shoppers Discount With Book | 25% off instore

Taj B Couture "Fashion House"

Taj B Couture "Fashion House", named after owner Latrina Brown's children, is a boutique formerly located in downtown Forest Park. Birthed in 2006, this luxurious couture brand specializes in custom ready-to-wear, evening and special occasion fashion for both women and men of all sizes. Each design is hand crafted to perfection with fine fabric selections. Latrina is a creative designer who inherited her skills from her uncle in the late 1970's. She has participated in many national runway shows and has drawn creative inspirations from places such as NYC, Paris, San Francisco, and Los Angeles. Her drive to bring global fashion concepts to the city of Chicago is based on the desire to see her customers styled in her whimsical designs. You can find a host of luxurious handbags, jewelry, accessories for women, and a small assortment of bags and ties for men on her website.

Address| N/A
Phone| 708- 646-7254
Hours| N/A
Email| tajbcouture@yahoo.com
Price range| $$-$$$$
Website| www.tajbcouture.com/
FB| Taj B Couture | @ OneCouturier
IG| Taj_b_couture
First Time Shoppers Discount With Book | 15% instore only

Near by boutiques not featured in this publication:

Epyk Luxury Boutique | 7446 Madison St, Forest Park, IL 60130| 708-435-4145
www.epykluxcollection.com/

Keeping the Faith Boutique | 7535 Roosevelt Rd, Forest Park, IL 60130| 312-522-0159

Suit Plus More

Ladies if there were ever a place for all things, dressy, elegant and classic --then Suit Plus More is it! Located in a west suburb just outside of Chicago in Hillside, IL, the Edwards family enjoys running their fun chic store selling everything from African attire to blinged out t-shirts. This store features a variety of church-style suits, hats, and accessories for both women and men. This is not the place to shop without taking granny along for a dose of vibrant colorful garments for her favorite holiday and social occasion. Their motto is simple: "Looking Good is Feeling Good" and you can't help not to, after your first visit.

Address| 4219 Butterfield Road, Ste 1A, Hillside, Illinois 60162
Hours| Tue-Fri:11am - 7pm | Sat:10am - 7pm Sun-Mon:Closed
Phone| 708- 240-4323 | 888-712-6362
Email| suitplusmore@gmail.com
Price range| $$-$$$
Website| www.suitplusmore.com | www.Suitplusmorefashion.com
FB| Suitplusmore Boutique Hillside IL | @ SuitPlusMore
IG| Suitplusmore
First Time Shoppers Discount With Book | 10% instore

Lure Boutique

What started out as a women's shoe store 7 years ago --owner Contessa Houston has now metamorphosed into a merchandise wonder offering very vibrant women's clothing, shoes and accessories right outside of Chicago in the Western suburbs. With the addition of clothing, the store revamped its slogan to: "Be Bold, Be Courageous, Be Confident, BeLured" --and they're doing just that by offering unique, quality one of a kind special occasion clothing for prom clients and uber trendy head turning everyday fashion. This store carries it all from freshwater pearls, 10 carat gold, high-end fashion jewelry, leather accessories, quality frames and curated items. It's a girl's one stop shop. Did I mention that they feature national cosmetic brands such as Real Her, a small selection of name brand children's shoes, and a seasonal collection of high-end furs/leather goods? What are you waiting for?! It's your time to get Lured in at this boutique!

Address| 224 Yorktown Shopping Center, Lombard, IL 60148
Phone| 630-216-9438
Hours| Mon-Sat: 10am-9pm | Sun: 11am-6pm.
Email| N/A
Size range| Small-3x | shoes sizes 5.5 to 11
Price range| $-$$ | Seasonal Fur: $$$-$$$$
Website| www.iShopLURE.com
FB| Shop LURE | @ishoplure
IG| ishoplure
First Time Shoppers Discount With Book | 19% off of total orders

MS. CATWALK BOUTIQUE LOCATION #2 | see pg63

The Ladies Room Consignment Resale Boutique

The Ladies Consignment Boutique

Catrina Kagel, a veteran in the fashion industry and of native of the West suburbs of Chicago, is the creative owner of this ladies only boutique located in Lombard, IL. This cool resale and women's consignment shop features a variety of pre-owned women's fashion in career, casual, and formal attire including a fabulous vintage selection from the 1920's through the 80's. Unlike your traditional resale shop, this shop accepts clothing based on quality and style in addition to your favorite designer brands nationwide. Driven by charity, you can find this boutique supporting a number of local organizations including a scholarship foundation the owner started to give music and art scholarships to low-income individuals living in Dupage County.

Address| 410 S. Main Street, Lombard, IL 60148
Hours| Mon- Fri:10am-7pm Sat: 10am-5pm Sun: Closed
Phone| 630-613-9593
Email| ck@thelroom.com
Website| www.thelroom.com
Price range| $-$$
FB| The Ladies Consignment Boutique | @tlrresale
IG| N/A
First Time Shoppers Discount With Book | 20% off regular priced merchandise

Ladies and Gentlemen Boutique

If you're looking for the ultimate luxury shop, this forest Park, IL boutique features a variety of upscale clothing from designer dress suits, minks, furs, and accessories for both ladies and gents. From popular brands like Donna Vincci, this family operated business has been serving West suburban Chicagoland since its inception in 1993 in Broadview, IL. Pastor Willie Brown is not a stranger to offering the quality merchandise and superior customer service that has stood the test of time and fashion. From first ladies, pastors, elite business professionals --customers dial in from all over the country. The store also offers custom apparel and convenient online shopping. This boutique is perfect for those who like trendy, classic, and all things lux. Shop like a lady or gentlemen here!

Address| 7929 W Cermak Road, North Riverside, Illinois 60546
Hours| Mon-Sat:10am-7pm | Sat:10am-6 pm | Sun: Closed
Phone| 708- 209-4600
Price range| $$-$$$$
Website| www.ladiesngentlemen'shop.com/
FB| Ladies & Gentlemen, Inc.
IG| N/A
First Time Shoppers Discount With Book | N/A

Chic Chick's Boutique

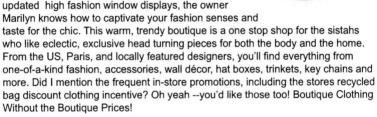

Admittedly, one of my favorite West suburban boutiques to drop in on is Chic Chick's Boutique located on Oak Park Ave in Oakpark, IL just minutes away from the I 290 West of Chicago. The Pink decorated exterior and interior store is a hidden treasure find. With frequently updated high fashion window displays, the owner Marilyn knows how to captivate your fashion senses and taste for the chic. This warm, trendy boutique is a one stop shop for the sistahs who like eclectic, exclusive head turning pieces for both the body and the home. From the US, Paris, and locally featured designers, you'll find everything from one-of-a-kind fashion, accessories, wall décor, hat boxes, trinkets, key chains and more. Did I mention the frequent in-store promotions, including the stores recycled bag discount clothing incentive? Oh yeah --you'd like those too! Boutique Clothing Without the Boutique Prices!

Address| 819 S.Oak Park Ave, Oak Park, IL 60302
Hours| Tues-Sat:12pm-6:30pm | Sun-Mon:Closed
Phone| 708- 524-1445
Email| chic.chicks.boutique@gmail.com
Price range| $-$$$
FB| Chic Chicks Boutique
IG| Chic_chicksboutique
First Time Shoppers Discount With Book | N/A

Let's Do It Again Resale Boutique

Shopping second-hand can be extremely rewarding for the budget conscious sistahs. Let's Do It Again Resale Boutique has been serving the Oak Park, IL community for over 20 years and is known for housing stylish and affordable jewelry, shoes, and fabulous vintage hats. Owner and tailor, Rose, has just the right assortment of gently worn clothing from sizes small to full-figured. The store is currently home to one of Chicago's famous milliners. The boutique offers all of your favorite silhouettes from the previous seasons, years, and decades. This is the place that will let you do it again and save!

Address| 319 Madison Street, Oak Park, IL 60302
Hours| Tue- Sat: 12pm -7pm | Sun:Closed
Phone| 312- 848-0153
Email| rose@letsdoitagainresaleboutique.com
Price range| $-$$$
Website| www.letsdoitagainresaleboutique.com/
FB| Let's Do It Again Resale/Consignment Boutique
IG| Let's Do It Again Resale/Consignment Boutique
First Time Shoppers Discount With Book | N/A

Perfect Fit Fashions & Accessories

This family owned boutique, founded by Sonja Clayborn is conveniently located on Madison – the hallmark street of fashion right outside of Chicago. The store is dedicated to the memory of their sister Gina who passed and has been carrying her sense of style throughout the shop since it opened in 2012. The trendy, contemporary store carries affordable clothing for the workplace or any social event. Women of various body types can expect to find the latest must have fashions, shoes, jewelry, and hosiery. Perfect Fit Fashions serves its fashionistas with personal styling, promotions, and online shopping. What's really cool is that their special events and charitable awareness serves social health groups such as the American Heart Association, breast cancer awareness, diabetes, and the special needs of women in their community.

Address| N/A
Hours| Online
Phone| 708- 848-4208
Email| perfectfitfashion@ymail.com
Price range| $-$$$
Sizes| XS-5x
Website| www.perfectfitfashion4u.com/
FB| Perfect Fit Fashion & Accessories | @pffginastyles
IG| Perfect Fit Fashion & Accessories
First Time Shoppers Discount With Book | 15% instore use code PFF15 online

<u>Pursenalaties Handbags & Jewelry</u>

Every handbag has a "pursenality" and owner Camesha knows how to showcase them front and center. This handbag and jewelry boutique located in Oak Park, IL boutique is a fashionista's dream accessory land with bags in chic textures, designs, and prints. Just as popular as the bags, there's oversized jewelry and a small display of fabulous t-shirts you can find. This shop is also a good choice for hosting birthday shopping parties, sip and shops and a good ole girl's night out all in one location. You can let your fashion pursenality shine forth after a quick whim of this trendy little store surrounded by other nearby beauty salons in reach of a total style makeover!

Address| 315 1/2 Madison Street,, Oak Park, IL 60302
Hours| Tue-Sat: 1pm-7pm | Sun-Mon: Closed
Price Range| $-$$$
Size Range| T-shirts-XS-2X (S-3X)
FB| Pursenalities handbags and jewelry| @PursesJewelry
First Time Shoppers Discount| 10% Instore

Near by boutiques not featured in this publication:

Brown Elephant Resale Shop | 217 Harrison St, Oak Park, IL 60304 | 708- 445-0612
www.howardbrown.org/get-involved/brown-elephant/
Dye Hard Yarns | 210 Harrison st unit A, Oak Park, IL 60304 | 708--613-4456
www.dyehardyarns.com/
Elegant Fashions | 104c Madison St, Oak Park, IL 60302 | 708-524-1877
Studio144 | 144 Harrison St, Oak Park, IL 60304 | 708-205-2866
V's Fashionable Boutique | 6924 Roosevelt Rd,Oak Park, IL 60304 | 708- 948-7425

BOUTIQUE DISCOUNTS

Chicago Boutique Discounts listed alphabetically

* Please note that discounts apply to Chicago fashion boutiques only where applicable.
Discounts are subject to owner's discretion based on current promotions that may overlap
discounts presented in this book publication. The author is neither reliable nor responsible
for the reader's misinterpretation of shopping incentives and all discounts listed represent
all stores' consent to discounts prior to the publication of this book.
Please inquire about the discounts prior to purchase at each store by presenting a copy
of this book both in print/ digitally or online code at point of purchase.

A Lot of Good Stuff	Bronzeville	20% in store
Absolutely Anything Essential Boutique	Bronzeville	20% in store, online pick up in store
Agriculture	Gold Coast	N/A
Anjels Boutique	Homewood, IL	10% in store/online
Annie Bell Fragrances	Chicagoland	N/A
Avante Garde Boutique	Forest Park, IL	25% in store
Barbara Bates Designs	South Loop	10% in store/online
Belle UP	Beverly	N/A
Borris Powell	West Loop	20% RTW, 10% Custom in store
Brims & Accessories	Chatham-Avalon	10% in store
Bronzeville Boutique By Lady Mocha	Bronzeville	10% online surprise discount in store
Chic Chick's Boutique	Oak park	N/A
Culture Closet Boutique	Beverly	N/A
Custom By Lamar	Near west side	10% in store
Dez De Mee House of Styles	Beverly	15% in store/online
Effortless Style Boutique	Avalon Park	10% in store/online
Ellana Boutique	Chatham-Park Manor	15% in store
Essential Elements	Chatham-Avalon	10% in store/online
Get Eyed Boutique	Evanston, IL	15% online
Fort Smith Boutique	Bronzeville	N/A
GILDA Designer Thrift Boutique	Hyde Park	10% in store
Glam Fashion Love	Near west side	5% in store/online
Goree Shop	Bronzeville	10% in store
Hyfaluten Boutique	Berwyn, IL	10% in store
Iridium Clothing	Downtown	10% in store/online
Island Furs	Beverly	40-70% merchandise in store

Jermikko Design Studio & Production	Downtown	N/A
Kayra Imports	Chattam-Avalon	10% in store
Kham'ryn B. Shoes	Auburn Gresham	15% in store/online
Kilimanjaro International	Hyde Park	10% in store/online
Kiwis Boutique	Near West Side	15% in store/online
Ladies and Gentlemen Boutique	Forest Park, IL	N/A
Let's Do It Again Resale Boutique	Oak Park, IL	N/A
Looks & Style Boutique	Chattham-Avalon	10% in store
Lure Boutique	Lombard, IL	19% off of total orders
Maxine's Boutique	Avalon Park	10% in store
Miami Paris	Galewood	15% in store
Momadou's Jewelry & Clothing	Downtown	10% in store
MS Cat Walk	South Loop	15% in store/online
Perfect Fit Fashions	Oak Park, IL	15% in store/online
Perfect Pieces	South Shore	10% in store/online
Pmarie Bridal Boutique	Bridgeport	$5 rebate
Pursenalaties	Oak Park, IL	10% instore
Rosebud Reflections	Greater Grand Crossing	10% in store
Sarah Kuenyefu	Woodlawn	10% in store/online
Shernett Swaby	River North	$100 off first purchase
Silver Room	Hyde Park	10% in store/online
Sir & Madam Hyde Park	Hyde Park	N/A
Sole Resale Boutique	Near West Side	10% in store
Stampley's Executive Salon	Hyde Park	15% in store
Stepping out on Faith Consignment	Evanston, IL	20% in store
Style Room 326	Lakeview	15% off $100 purchase
Succezz	South Loop	10% in store
Suit Plus More	Hillside, IL	10% in store
Sullivan's Fashions	South Shore	10-20% daily in store
Taj B Design	Forest Park, IL	N/A
Teresa Fe-Fe Designs	Crete, IL	10% in store/by appointment
The Ladies Consignment Boutique	Lombard, IL	20% off regular price merchandise in store
Wesley Shoes	Hyde Park	N/A
Wired The Design Boutique	Flossmoor IL	15% in store/online

Body Oil Scrubs Butters Shower Gels Soaps

Art Galleries | Bookstores | Museums | Theaters

ART GALLERIES
NEIGHBORHOOD| BRONZEVILLE

Blanc
Address| 4445 S. Martin Luther King Dr.,
        Chicago, IL 60653
Hours| Sat: 1pm-3pm
Phone| 773-373-4320
Website| www.blancchicago.com/
FB| Blanc Gallery
IG| Blanc Gallery Chicago

Faie Afrikan Art in Bronzeville
Address| 1005 E. 43rd St, Chicago, IL
        60653
Hours| Mon-Tue | By Appointment Only
        Wed- Fri 11:00am-6:00pm
        Sat-12pm-6:30:pm Sun | Closed
Phone| 773.268.2889
Email| Faie@ATT.NET
Website| www.faieafrikanart.com/
FB| Faie African Art in Bronzeville
IG| GalleryGuichardSocial

Gallery Guichard
Address| 436 E.47th ST, Chicago, IL
        60653
Hours| Wed 2pm-5pm | Fri: 1pm-5pm
        Thurs: Closed | Sat: 12pm-3pm
        Sun: Tue Closed
Phone| 708-772-9315
Email| galleryguichardsocial@gmail.com
Website| www.galleryguichard. com/
FB| Gallery Guichard
IG| GalleryGuichardSocial

Little Black Pearl
Address| 1060 E. 47th ST, Chicago, IL
        60653
Hours| Mon- Fri:10am-6pm
        Sat-Sun: Closed
Phone| 773-285-1211
Email| info@blackpearl.org
Website| www.blackpearl.org
FB| Little Black Pearl
IG| _Blackpearlarts

South Side Community Art Center
Address| 3831 S. Michigan Ave.
        Chicago, IL 60653
Hours| Wed-Fri: 12pm-5:00pm
        Sat: 9am-5pm | Sun: 1pm-5pm
        Mon-Tues: Closed
Phone| 773-373-1026
Email| info@sscartcenter.org
Website| www.sscartcenter.org/
FB| South Side Community Art Center
IG| South Side Community Art Center

BOOK STORES
NEIGHBORHOOD| CHATHAM/AVALON

Da Book Joint
Address| 2311 E. 71st ST, Chicago, IL
        60649
Hours| Thurs-Fri: 10am-6pm
        Sat: 10am-5:30pm
Phone| 773-655-3146
Email| verlean@dabookjoint.com
Website| www.dabookjoint.com
FB| Da Book Joint
IG| Da Book Joint

Underground Bookstore
Address| 1727 E.87th
ST,Chicago, IL 60617
Hours| Mon-Sat 11am-7pm
        Sun: 11am-5pm
Phone| 773-768-8869
Email| theunderground
        bookstore@gmail.com
Website| www.semicolonchi.com
FB| Underground Bookstore

NEIGHBORHOOD| HYDE PARK

Frontline Book Store
Address| 5206 S.Harper Ave
        Chicago, IL 60615
Hours| Mon-Thurs: 10am-8pm
        | Fri-Sat: 10am-9pm Sun: 11am-
        7pm
Phone| 773-288-7718
Email| frontlinebooks@gmail.com
Website| www.frontlinebookpublishing.
        com/
FB| frontline books Hyde Park
IG| frontline_books

97

Beauty Supply Stores | Nail Salons | Cafes & Restaurants

Frontline Books & Kultural Emporium
Address| 6357 S. Cottage Grove Ave.,
Chicago, IL 60615
Hours| Mon-Sat: 11am-7pm
Sun: 11am-6pm
Phone| 872-244-3242
Email| frontlinetheemporium@gmail.com
Website| www.frontlinebookpublishing.
com/
FB| Frontline Books & Kultural Emporium
IG| frontlinetheemporium

NEIGHBORHOOD| SOUTH SHORE

ETA Creative Arts Foundation
Address| 7558 S. South Chicago Ave,
Chicago, IL 60619
Hours| Mon-Fri: 10am-6pm
Sat-Sun: Closed
Phone| 773- 752-3955
Email| info@etacreativearts.org
Website| www.etacreativearts.org/
FB| Eta Creative Arts
IG| EtacreativeArtsFoundation

Muntu Dance Theater of Chicago
Address| 1809 E. 71 ST, STE 203
Chicago, IL 60649
Hours| check online
Phone| 773-241-6080
Email| Sekou@muntu.com
Website| Muntu.com
FB| Muntu Dance Theatre of Chicago
IG| MuntuDance

NEIGHBORHOOD| UPTOWN

Black Ensemble Theater
Address| 4450 N. Clark ST, Chicago, IL
60640
Hours| Mon-Fri-10am-6pm
Sat-11:00-8pm Sun: 1pm-5:30pm
Phone| 773-769-4451
Email| boxoffice@blackensemble.org
Website| blackensembletheater.org/
FB| Black Ensemble Theater
IG| BlackEnsemble

BEAUTY SUPPLY STORES
NEIGHBORHOOD| AUBURN GRESHAM

BJ's Beauty Solutions Supply & Salon Inc.
Address| 8704 S. Loomis St, Chicago,IL
60620
Phone| 773-779-7100
Hours| Tues-Sat: 8:30am-6pm Sun- Mon:
Closed
Email| yourbeautysolutions@aol.com
FB| BJ's Beauty Solutions Supply & Salon
Inc.
IG| BJ's Beauty Solutions Supply & Salon
Inc.

Sam's Beauty Supply
Address| 8701 S. Racine Ave.
Chicago, IL 60620
Phone| 773-779-8287
Hours| Mon -Sat: 8am-10pm | Sun:
9am-7pm
FB| Sam's Beauty Supply
IG| Sam's Beauty Supply

NEIGHBORHOOD| CHATHAM

Solo Beauty Supply
Address| 8158 S. Cottage Grove Ave,
Chicago, IL
Phone| 773-723-0533
Hours| Tues-Wed: 3pm-7pm | Thurs-Sat:
12pm-8pm Sun: Closed
Email| solobeautysupply@gmail.com
Website| www.solobeautysupply.com
FB| SOLO Beauty Supply
IG| SOLO Beauty Supply

NEIGHBORHOOD| CHATHAM/SOUTHSHORE

Jordan's Beauty Supply
Address| 1911 E. 79th St, Chicago, IL
60649
Phone| 773-734-6268
Hours| Sun-Tues: Closed | Wed-Sat:
10am-3pm
Email| info@jordanbeautysupply.com
Website| wwwjordansbeautysupply.com/
FB| Jordan's Beauty Supply
IG| JordansBeautySupply

NEIGHBORHOOD| ROGER'S PARK

I M Beauty Supply
Address| 1609 N.Howard ST,
Chicago, IL 60626
Phone| 773- 564-9788
Hours| Mon-Sat: 11am-6pm
Sun: 11am-5pm
Email| service@imbeautysupply.com
Website| www.imbeautysupply.com/
FB| MBeautyChicago
IG| IMBeautyChicago

NEIGHBORHOOD WESTSIDE CHICAGO

Dazzle N Style Beauty Supply
Address| 4326 W. Division ST,
Chicago, IL 60651
Phone| 773-799-8218
Hours| Mon-Sat: 10am-7pm
Sun: Closed
FB| Dazzle N Style Beauty Supply
IG| DazzleNStyleBeautySupply

WEST SUBURBS OAK PARK, IL

House of Melanin
Address| 262 Chicago Ave.
Oak Park, IL 60302
Phone| 708-864-0004
Hours| Tues-Sat: 12pm-5pm
Sun-Mon: Closed
Email| info@houseofmelaninbeauty.com
Website| www.thehouseofmelanin.com
FB| House of Melanin
IG| Houseofmelanin

NAIL/SPA BOUTIQUES NEIGHBORHOOD| AUSTIN

Bottom Nail Salon
Address| 5624 W. Chicago Ave.
Chicago, IL 60644
Phone| 773- 378-5322
Hours| Mon-Sat: 10am-7pm
Sun: Closed
FB| Bottom Nail Salon The 1 & 2
IG| Bottom Nail Salon The 1 & 2

NEIGHBORHOOD| AVALON

Effortless Boutique Pamper Suites
Location# 1
Address| 424 E. 87th ST, Chicago, IL
60619
Hours| Tues-Sat: 11am-7pm
Sun-Mon: Closed
Phone| 773-902-1900
Website| www.effortlessboutique.com/
Fb| Effortless Boutique
Ig| Effortless Boutique

Location #2 Bronzeville Neighborhood
Address| 3960 S. Cottage Grove
Chicago, IL 60619
Hours| Tues-Sat: 11am-7pm
Sun-Mon: Closed
Phone| 773-268-0800

Lux Nail Boutique
Address| 8206 S. Stony Island Ave,
Chicago, IL 60617
Phone| 773-437-4628
Hours| Mon-Fri: 10am- 8pm
Sat: 10am-7pm Sun: Closed
Email| support@luxnailboutique.com
Website| www.luxnailboutique.com/
FB| Lux Hair & Nail Boutique
IG| luxhairandnailboutique

NEIGHBORHOOD| BEVERLY

Charm'd by Char
Address| 2600 W. 99th ST, Chicago, IL
60655
Phone| 312-731-9764
Hours| Tues-Thus: 10am-7pm
Fri: 9am-7pm Sat: 6am-4pm
Sun-Mon: Closed
Email| info@charmedbychar.com
Website| www.charmedbychar.booksy.
com
FB| CHARMED By Char
IG| Charmed_by_char

NEIGHBORHOOD| BRONZEVILLE

MB Nail Lounge
Address| 1009 E. 43rd ST, Chicago, IL 60653
Phone| 773- 800-1746
Hours| Tues: 11am-4pm | Wed-Sat: 11am-7pm | Sun-Mon: Closed
Email| mbnaillounge@gmail.com
Website| www.mbnaillounge.com
FB| Nails by Meesha B
IG| mbluxurynaillounge

NEIGHBORHOOD| CHATHAM

A Polished Work
Address| 1000 E. 76th St, Chicago, IL 60619
Phone| 312-715-8870
Hours| Mon-Fri 10am-8pm Sat: 9am-7pm Sun: Closed
Email| apolishedwork@gmail.com
Website| www.apolishedwork.com/
FB| A Polished Work Inc.
IG| A Polished Work Inc

NEIGHBORHOOD| HUMBOLT

Pretty Dapper Day Spa & Wax Bar
Address| 818 N. California Ave. Chicago, IL
Phone| 773-413-9878
Hours| By Appointment Only
Email| renewed@prettydapperday.com
Website| www.prettydapperday.com/
FB| Pretty Dapper Day Spa & Wax Bar
IG| Prettydapperskin

NEIGHBORHOOD| PILSEN

Pear Nova Studio
Address| 2150 S .Canalport Ave., 4C, #14, Chicago, IL 60608
Phone| 312-248-8914
Hours| Tues-Sat: 11am-7pm Sun-Mon:Closed
Email| info@pearnova.com
Website| www.pearnova.com/
FB| Pear Nova Studio
IG| Pear Nova Studio

NEIGHBORHOOD| SOUTHLOOP

MJ2 Hair & Nail Boutique
Address| 2015 S.Indiana Ave, Chicago, IL 60616
Phone| 312-450-3947
Hours| Tues-Sat: 9am -7pm Sun-Mon: Closed
Website| www.mj2hairandnailboutique.com/
FB| Mj2 Hair & Nail Boutique
IG| Mj2 Hair & Nail Boutique

NEIGHBORHOOD| WOODLAWN

Beautiful Sisters Nail Spa
Address| 6722 S. Stony Island Ave, Chicago, IL 60649
Phone| 773-359-4174
Hours| Mon-Tues: 10:30am-7pm
Wed: 10:30am-5pm
Thurs: 10:30am-7pm
Fri-Sat: 10:30am-8pm | Sun:Closed
Email| beautifulsistersnail@gmail.com
Website| sisterspa.com
FB| Beautiful Sisters Nail Spa
IG| Beautiful Sisters Nail Spa

SOUTH SUBURBS CALUMET, IL

Tre Bella Nail Spa
Address| 12545 S. Ashland Ave, Calumet Park, IL 60827
Phone| 708- 897-9060
Hours| Tues-Fri: 10am-7pm
Email| MSMPRICE02@YAHOO.COM
Website| www.trebellanailspa.com/
FB| Tre'Bella Nail Spa
IG| Tre'Bella Nail Spa

SOUTH SUBURBS MATTESON IL

Perfectionist Nails
Address| 21516 Main Street Matteson, IL
Phone| 773- 209-3689
Hours| Tues: 9am-7pm | Wed: Closed
Thurs-Fri: 9am-7pm
Sat: 9am-5pm | Sun-Mon: Closed
FB| Perfectionist Nails
IG| Perfectionist Nails

Please Note: A ❤ next to a listing symbolizes one of the author's favorite places to dine

WEST SUBURBS OAK PARK, IL

Glitter Nail Salon
Address| 912 Madison St, Oak Park, IL
60302
Phone| 708- 613-5322
Hours| Tues- Fri: 10am-7pm
Sat-8am-5pm | Sun-Mon: Closed
Email| glitternailsalon@gmail.com
Website | www.myglitternailsalon.com/
FB| Glitter Nail Salon
IG| Glitter Nail Salon

CAFÉS & RESTUARANT

Lexington Betty Smoke House
Location #1
Address| 6954 W. North Ave,
Chicago, IL 60707
Phone| 773-309-8240
Hours| Wed-Sat: 12pm-5pm
Sun-Mon: Closed

Location #2
Pullman Neighborhood
Address| 756 E. 111th St. (Inside the One
Eleven Food Hall)

Location #3
Near Westside
Dr. Murphy's Food Hall
Address| 1835 W. Harrison St. Chicago
IL 60612
Phone| N/A
Hours| Sun-Thurs: 11am-9pm
Fri-Sat: 11am-10:30pm
Email| Dominiqueleach@
catertoyouevents.net
Website | www.lexingtonbettysmoke-
house.com/
FB| Lexington Betty Smoke House #1
IG| Lexington Betty Smoke House

NEIGHBORHOOD| AUBURN GRESHAM

Haire's Gulf Shrimp ❤
Address| 7448 S. Vincennes
Ave, Chicago, IL 60620
Phone| 773-783-1818
Hours| Mon: 11am-8pm | Tues-Sat:
11am-9pm Sun: 12pm-6pm
Email| aishsm1@msn.com
FB| Haire's Gulf Shrimp
IG| haires_gulf_shrimp

Q's Tips & Wings Bar B Que
Address| 2517 W. 79th ST, Chicago, IL
60652
Phone| 773- 912-6498
Website| www.qstipsandwings.com
FB| Q's Tips & Wings Bar B Que

NEIGHBORHOOD| AVALON

5 Loaves Eatery
Address| 405 E. 75th ST, Chicago, IL
60619
Phone| 773 891-2889
Email| 5loaveschicago@gmail.com
Website| www.5loaveschicago.com/
FB| 5 Loaves Eatery

Anita's Gumbo **(Express Carry out)**
Address| 8100 S. Stony Island,
Chicago, IL 60617
Phone| 773-734-2788
Website | www.nitasgumbo.com/
FB| Nita's Gumbo

Location #2
Country Club Hills Location Dine In
Address| 4153 W.183rd Street, Country
Club Hills, IL
Phone| 708-960-0530

Brown Sugar Bakery ❤
Address| 328 E.75th ST, Chicago, IL
60619
Hours| Please see website
Phone| 773- 224-6262
Location #2
Address| 4800 W. Chicago Ave.,
Chicago 60651
Email| brownsugarbakery75@gmail.com
Website | www.brownsugarbakerychicago.
com/
FB| Brown Sugar Bakery-Chicago

101

BJ's Market & Bakery
Address| 8734 S. Stony Island Ave.
Chicago, IL 60617
Hours| Mon-Sat: 11am-9pm
Sun: 11am-8pm
Phone| 773-374-4700
Email| soulfood@bjsmarket.com| Info@
bjsmarket.com
Website| www.bjsmarket.com
FB| BJ's Market & Bakery
IG| Bjs_market

Location #2
Address| 1156 W. 79th Street,
Chicago, IL 60620

NEIGHBORHOOD| BEVERLY

Flippin Flavors
Address| 1848 W. 95th Street
Chicago, IL 60643
Phone| 773-253-2680
Website| www.flippinflavors.com
FB| Flippin Flavors

Ohana Ice & Treats
Address| 1800 W.103rd St, Chicago, IL
60643
Phone| 773-253-8533
Email| ohanaiceandtreats@gmail.com
Website| N/A
FB| Ohanaicechicago

NEIGHBORHOOD| BRONZEVILLE

Ain't She Sweet Café
Address| 526 E. 43rd ST, Chicago, IL
60653
Hours| Mon-Fri: 10:am-6:00pm
Sat: 11-am-6:00pm | Sun: Closed
Phone| 773-373-3530
Email| contact@aintshesweetcafe.com
Website| www.aintshesweetcafe.com/
Location#2
Address| 9920 S. Western Ave
Chicago, IL 60643

Frii Style Chicago
Address| 5059 S. Prairie Ave,
Chicago, IL 60615
Phone| 773-548-5375
Website| www.friistylechicago.com/
FB| FriiStyle Chicago

Goree Cuisine
Address| 1126 E. 47th ST, Chicago IL
Phone| 773- 855-8120
Website| www.goreecuisine.com/
FB| GoreeCuisine

Honey BBQ
Address| 746 E. 43rd St, Chicago, IL
60653
Phone| 773-285-9455
Website| www.honey1bbq.com/
FB| Honey1bbq

Norman Bistro   ♥
Address| 1001 E 43rd St, Chicago, IL
60653
Hours| Wed-Sun: 2pm-10pm
Mon-Tues: Closed
Phone| 773-966-5821
Email| contactus@normansbistro.com
Website| www.normansbistro.com/
FB| Norman's Bistro
IG| Norman'sBistro

Peaches Restaurant   ♥
Address| 4652 S. King Dr., Chicago, IL
60653
Hours| Sun: 8am-2pm | Mon-Tues:
Closed Closed Major Holidays
Phone| 773-966-5801
Website| http://peachson47th.com/
FB| Peach's Restaurant
IG| Peaches Restaurant

Pearl's Place
Address| 3901 S. Michigan Ave,
Chicago, IL 60653
Phone| 877-275-5852
Website| www.pearlsplacerestaurant.
com/
FB| Pearl's Place Restaurant

Sip & Savor Chicago   ♥
Address| 528 E. 43rd St, Chicago, IL
60653
Hours| Mon-Sun: 8am-4pm
Phone| 773-855-2125
Email| info@sipandsavorchicago.com
Website| www.sipandsavorchicago.com/
FB| Sip & Savor Chicago
IG| SipandSavorChicago

Sip & Savor Chicago Continued ♥
Location #2 Hyde Park Neighborhood
Address| 5301 S. Hyde Park
(Del Prado Building)
Phone| 773-952-4532
Hours| Mon-Sun: 8am-4pm

Location #3 Rosenwald Neighborhood
Address| 78 E. 47th St, Chicago, IL
60653
Phone| 773-633-2722
Hours| Mon-Sun: 8am-4pm

Slice of Bronzeville
Address| 4655 S. King Dr, Chicago, IL
60653
Phone| 872- 244-7663
Website| www.Sliceofbronzeville.net
FB| Slice of Bronzeville

Some Like It Black Creative Arts Bar
Address| 810 E. 43rd St, Chicago, IL
60653
Hours| Tues, Thurs, Fri: 5pm-11pm
Sat: Special events only
Sun, Mon, Wed: Closed
Phone| 773-891-4866
Email| somelikeitblack@yahoo.com
Website| www.somelikeitblack.com/
FB| somelikeitblack
IG| somelikeitblack

| NEIGHBORHOOD| CHATHAM

Dat Donut
Address| 8251 S. Cottage Grove,
Chicago, IL 60619
Phone| 773-723-1002
Website| www.datdonut.com/
FB| Dat Donut

| NEIGHBORHOOD| GREAT GRAND CROSSING

The Woodlawn
Address| 1200 E. 79th St, Chicago, IL
60619
Phone| 773- 902-2470
Email| info@thewoodlawn1200.com
Website| www.thewoodlawn1200.com/
FB| TheWoodlawn

| NEIGHBORHOOD| GREAT GRAND CROSSING

The Woodlawn
Address| 1200 E. 79th St, Chicago, IL
60619
Phone| 773- 902-2470
Email| info@thewoodlawn1200.com
Website| www.thewoodlawn1200.com/
FB| TheWoodlawn

| NEIGHBORHOOD| HYDE PARK

Ja' Grill ♥
Address| 1510 E Harper Ct.,
Chicago, IL 60615
Hours| Sun-Wed: 11am-10pm|Thu-Sat:
11am-11pm Bar Hours: daily-2am
Phone| 773-752-5375
Email| info@jagrill.com
Website| www.jagrill.com/
FB| Ja' Grill Hyde Park
IG| JaGrillHyde Park

Kimbark BeverageShoppe
Address| 1214 E. 53rd St, Chicago, IL
60615
Phone| 773- 493-3355
Website| www.kimbarkbeverage.com/
FB| Kimbark Beverage Shopp

Mickeys Retro Grill
Address| 5319 S. Hyde Park BLVD
Chicago, IL 60615
Phone| 773 -675-8525
Website| www.mikkeys.com/
FB| Mikkeys Retro Grill

Location#2 Bronzeville Neighborhood
Address| 503 East 47th, Chicago, IL
60653
Phone| 773- 952-4082
Location#3 Avalon Neighborhood
Address| 8126 S .Stony Island
Chicago, IL
Phone| 773-902-2800

Soul Shack
Address| 1368 E 53rd St, Chicago, IL
60615
Phone| 773-891-0126
Website| www.thesoul53.com/
FB| The Soul Shack

Virtue Restaurant ♥
Address| 1462 E. 53rd St, Chicago, IL
60615
Phone| 773 947-8831
Hours| Wed-Sun:4pm-9pm
Mon-Tues:Closed
Email| info@virtuerestaurant.com
Website| www.virtuerestaurant.com/
FB| VirtueRestaurant
IG| VirtueRestaurantchi

NEIGHBORHOOD| NEAR WEST SIDE

Sweet Maple Cafe
Address| 1339 W. Taylor Street
Chicago, IL 60607
Phone| 312-243-8908
Website| www.sweetmaplecafe.com/
FB| Sweet Maple Cafe Chicago

NEIGHBORHOOD| LINCOLN PARK

Batter & Berries ♥
Address| 2748 N. Lincoln Ave,
Chicago, IL 60614
Hours| Mon-Sun: 8am-3pm
Phone| 773-248-7710
Email| info@batterandberries.com
Website| www.batterandberries.com/
FB| Batter & Berries
IG| BatterandBerries

NEIGHBORHOOD| LINCOLN SQUARE

Luellas Southern Kitchen
Address| 4609 N. Lincoln Ave
Chicago, IL 60625
Phone| 773 961-8196
Website| www.luellassouthernkitchen.
com
FB| Luella's Southern Kitchen

NEIGHBORHOOD| UKRANIAN VILLAGE

Soule Chicago
Address| 931 W. Chicago Ave
Chicago, IL 60622
Phone| 312- 526-3825
Website| www.soulechicago.com/
FB| Soulé Chicago

NEIGHBORHOOD| CHATHAM

Demera Ethopian Cuisine ♥
Address| 4801 N. Broadway street
Chicago, IL 60640
Phone| 773-334-8787
Hours| Sun-Thurs: 12pm-9pm | Fri-Sat:
12pm-10pm
Email| info@demerachicago.com
Website| www.demerachicago.com/
FB| Demera Ethiopian
IG| demeraethiopianchi

Grace's African Restaurant
Address| 4409 N.Broadway,
Chicago, IL 60640
Phone| 773-271-6000
Website www.graceafricanrestaurant.
com/
FB| Grace African Restaurant

Iyanze Bar And Cafe
Address| 4623 N. Broadway, Chicago,
IL 60640
Phone| 773- 944-1417
Website| N/A
FB| Iyanze African Cuisine & Bar

The Mukase African Restaurant ♥
Address| 1363 W. Wilson Ave,
Chicago, IL 60640
Phone| 773- 754-7121
Hours| Tues-Sun: 11am-7pm
Email| themukaseresturant@gmail.com
Website| www.themukase.com
FB| The Mukase Restaurant
IG| The Mukase Restaurant

NEIGHBORHOOD| CHATHAM

Eleven Elven
Address| 1111 W. Lake St, Chicago, IL
60607
Phone| 312- 248-8942
Website| www.elevenelevenchicago.com/
FB| Eleven Eleven Chicago

NEIGHBORHOOD| CHATHAM

Taste 222 ♥
Address| 222 N. Canal St, Chicago, IL
60606
Phone| 312-383-6620
Hours| Mon-Fri: 12pm-7pm
Sat-Sun: Closed
Email| Kmorris@taste222.com
Website| www.taste222chicago.com
FB| Taste 222 Chicago
IG| Taste 222 Chicago

Vegan Now
Address| 131 N. Clinton St, Chicago, IL
60661
Website| www.frenchmarketchicago.com/
vendor/vegan-now/
FB| Vegan Now
IG| VeganNowChicago

Location#2 Avalon/Chatham
Address| 201-209 E. 75th Street,
Chicago, IL
Phone| 773-224-0104
Website| www.soulvegcity.com/
FB| Soul Vegetarian Restaurant

SOUTH SUBURBS| DOLTON, IL

Kozy Korner Deli
Address| 15443 S. Cottage Grove
Phone| 708-955-1200
Website| www.kozykatering.com
FB| Kozy korner 2

SOUTH SUBURBS| HAZEL CREST

Pink Panini Soups & Salads ♥
Address| 17505 Kedzie Ave, Hazel Crest,
IL 60429
Phone| 708- 914-4331
Website| www.pinkpaninisoupsandsal-
ads.com
FB| Pink Panini Soups & Salad

SOUTH SUBURBS| MATTESON, IL

Dusties Southern Style Buffet
Address| 4012 Lincoln Highway,
Matteson, IL 60466
Phone| 708-228-5500
Hours| Mon-Sun: 11am-9pm
Website| www.dustiesbuffet.com
FB| Dusties Southern Style Buffet
IG| Dusties Southern Style Buffet

Hidden Manna Cafe
Address| 3613 W. 216th ST, Matteson,
IL 60443
Phone| 708-248-5571
Website| www.hiddenmannacafe.com
FB| Hidden Manna Cafe

NEIGHBORHOOD| MIDLOTHIAN, IL

Juiced By Shic
Address| 14736 Pulaski RD, Midlothian,
IL 60445
Phone| 708-897-8068
Location #2 Palos Heights| IL
Address| 12801 S. Harlem Ave,
Palos Heights, IL 60463
Phone| 708-827-5344
Hours| Mon-Fri: 8am-7pm | Sat:
9am -5pm | Sun: Closed
Website| www.juicedbyshic.com
FB| JuicedbyShic

WEST SUBURBS| FOREST PARK

Harvest 365 Restaurant & Fresh Grill ♥
Address| 7610 W. Roosevelt Rd Suite
120, Forest Park, IL 60130
Phone| 708- 488-0415
Hours| Tues-Sun: 11am-6pm Mon:
Closed
Email| info@harvest365grill.com
Website| www.harvest365grill.com/
FB| Harvest 365 Restaurant & Fresh Grill
IG| Harvest 365 Restaurant & Fresh Grill

NEIGHBORHOOD| HILLSIDE, IL

Priscilla's Ultimate Soul Food

Address| 4330 W. Roosevelt Rd Hillside,
　　　　IL 60162
Hours| Sun: 11am-8pm Open On Easter,
　　　　Mothers Day, Fathers Day
Phone| 708-544-6230
Website| www.priscillasultimatesoulfood.
　　　　com/index.html
FB| Priscilla's Ultimate Soulfood Cafeteria
IG| Priscilla's Ultimate Soulfood Cafeteria
Location#2 Hanover Park,IL
Priscilla's Ultimate Express
Address| 1840 W. Army Trail Rd Hanover
　　　　Park, IL 60133
Phone| 630-540-2040
FB| Priscilla's Ultimate Express
IG| Priscilla's Ultimate Express
Location#3 Hazel Crest, IL
Address| 3840 West 183 St Hazel Crest,
　　　　IL 60429
Phone| 708-957-1433
FB| Priscilla's Ultimate Soul Food #3
IG| Priscilla's Ultimate Soul Food #3

WEST SUBURBS| OAK PARK, IL

Robinson No.1 Ribs ♥

Address| 848 Madison, Oak Park, IL
　　　　60302
Hours| Mon-Thurs: 11am-10pm
　　　　Fri-Sat: 11am-12am| Sun:12pm-
　　　　9pm, Sunday Buffet: 12pm-6pm
Phone| 708-383-8452
Email | sales@rib1.com
Website| www.rib1.com/
FB| Robinson No.1 Ribs
IG| Robinson No.1 Ribs

BONUS

ATLANTA, GA

TAGS BOUTIQUE
Address| 177 Peters St SW, Atlanta, GA
  30313
Hours| Fri-Sat:11am-6pm
  Sun:12pm-5pm | Mon: 11am-6pm
  Tues-Thurs: Closed
Phone| 404- 883-3836
Email| info@tagsatl.com
Price range| $-$$$
Size range| XS-3X
Website| www.tagsatl.com/
FB| Tags Boutique | @tagsboutique
IG| tagsboutique

Pink Sky Boutique
Address| 485 Bill Kennedy Way SE Suite
  D, Atlanta, GA 30316
Hours| Tues-Sat: 11am-7pm
Phone| 404-549-7047
Email| info@pinkskyboutique.com
Price range| $-$$$
Size range| XS-2X
Website| www.pinkskyboutique.com/
FB| Pink Sky Boutique Atlanta
IG| pinkskyboutique

Pressed
Address| 3500 Peachtree Rd., NE
  Atlanta, GA 30326
Hours| Mon-Sat: 10am-9pm EST
  Sun:12pm- 6pm EST
Phone| 404 330-8932
Price range| $$-$$$
Size range| S-3X
Email| dlo117@gmail.com
Website| www.pressedatl.com/
FB| Pressed ATL|@Pressed ATL
IG| pressedatl

Wilbourn Sisters Designs
Address| 134 Peachtree St. NW. Atlanta,
  GA 30303
Phone| 770-634-3494
Hours| Tues-Sat 11am-7pm
Email| Wilbournslegacy@gmail.com
Website| www.WilbournsistersDesigns.
  com
FB| Wilbournsisters
IG| Wilbournsistersdesigns
Location #2
Address| 4745 W. Slauson Ave.Los
  Angeles, CA. 90056
Phone| 770-631-3496
Hours| By Appointment

NEW YORK

Calabar Imports
Address| 708 Franklin Avenue,
  Brooklyn, NY
Hours| Mon, Wed-Sat: 11am-7:30pm
  Tues: Closed
Phone| 718-638-4288
Price range| $$-$$$
Email| info@calabar-imports.com
Website| www.calabar-imports.com
FB| Calabar Imports
IG| Calabarimportsbklyn

Location #2
Address| 351 Tompkins Avenue,
  Brooklyn, NY 11216
Hours| Wed-Sun: 11:30am-7pm
  Mon-Tues: Closed
Phone| 718-928-3970

Location #3
Address| 2504 Frederick Douglass Blvd,
  Harlem, NY 10030
Hours| Wed- Sat: 12pm-7:30pm |Sun:12
  pm-6pm | Mon-Tues: Closed
Phone| 646-964-5062

Marche Ru Dix
Address| 1453 Bedford Ave Brooklyn NY, 11216
Hours| Mon-Sat: 12pm-9pm
Sun: 11am-8pm
Phone| 347-414-5436
Price Range| $$-$$$
Email| marcheruedix@gmailcom
Website| www.marcheruedix.com/
FB| Marche Rue Dix
IG| marcheruedix

Style Eyes Optical
Address| 1005 Flatbush Ave, Brooklyn, NY 11226
Hours| Mon-Sat: 10am-7pm | Sun: Closed
Phone| 718- 942-5957
Price Range| $$-$$$
Email| styleeyesoptical@yahoo.com
Website| www.styleeyesoptical.com
FB| Style Eyes Optical
IG| styleeyesoptical

The Wrap Life
Address| 51 35th St, 2nd Floor Brooklyn, NY 11232
Hours| see website
Phone| 917-794-2350
Price Range| $$
Email| info@thewrap.life
Website| www.thewrap.life/
FB| The Wrap Life
IG| Thewraplife

HARLEM| NEW YORK

Brownstone Boutique NY
Address| 24 E 125th ST, New York, NY 10035
Hours| Mon-Sat: 11am-7:30pm | Sun: 1pm-6pm
Phone| 212-996-7980
Price Range| $$-$$$
Size Range| XS-3X
Email| thebrownstone125@gmail.com
Website| www.thebrownstonewoman.com/
FB| The Brownstone Woman
IG| Thebrownstonewoman

Harlem Haberdashery
Address| 245 Malcolm X Blvd, New York, NY 10027
Hours| Mon-Sat: 12pm-8pm | Sun: Closed
Phone| 646-707-0070
Price Range| $$-$$$
Email| Info@HarlemHaberdashery.com
Website| www.harlemhaberdashery.com/
FB| Harlem Haberdashery
IG| Haberdasherynyc

HIGHLAND, INDIANA

Ms. Elles's Especially Yours Boutique
Address| 2235 45th St, Highland, IN 46322
Hours| Tues-Sat: 11am-5pm | Sun: Closed
Phone| 219- 924-4204
Price Range| $$-$$$
Size Range| XS-3X
Email| ms.ellesespeciallyforyou@gmail.com
Website| www.ms-elles-especially-for-you.business.site/
FB| Ms. Elle's especially for you-Sophisticated, Stylish and Spiritual
IG| lorna.colette

MERRILLVILLE, INDIANA

Cynthia J Designs
Address| 7863 Broadway,suite 113 Broadway Office Merrillville, IN 46410
Hours| Tues-Sat: By Appointment Sun-Mon:Closed
Phone| 219-577-7239
Email| Designsbycynthiaj.com
Website| www.designsbycynthiaj.com
FB| Cynthia J Designs
IG| Cynthia J Designs

HOUSTON| TEXAS

I'MarE Boutique
Address| 246 FM 1960 Bypass Rd., E
Humble, TX 77338
Hours| Wed-Fri: 11am-6pm
Sat: 12pm-6pm | Sun-Tues: Closed
Phone| 713-418-9353
Price range| $$-$$$
Size range| S-3X
Email| imareboutique@gmail.com
Website| www.shopimareboutique.com/
FB| I'MarE Boutique
IG| Imareboutique

The House of Couture Houston
Address| 4444 Cypress creek park way
Houston ,Texas 77608
Hours| Tues-Fri: 11am-6pm
Sat: 10am-7pm | Sun: Closed
Phone| 281- 889-3845
Price range| $$-$$$
Size range| S-3X
Email| thehouseofcoutureboutique@
gmail.com
Website| www.shopthoc.com/
FB| The House of Couture Houston
IG| TheHouseofcouturehouston

Robi Girls Closet
Address| 12955 South Fwy #B11
Houston, Texas
Hours| Sun-Tues: By Appt | Wed-Thurs:
3:30pm-7pm
Phone| 713- 487-5614 | 832-781-0523
Price range| $$-$$$
Size range| XS-3X
Email| robigirlscloset@yahoo.com
Website| www.robigirlscloset.com/
FB| RobiGirls Closet
IG| robigirls13

Africa Imports Houston
Address| 2300 North Fwy #147,
Houston, TX 77060
Hours| Mon-Sat: 10am-9pm
Sun: 12pm-6pm
Phone| 281 875-0056
Price range| $-$$$
Size range| All Sizes
Email| donbasel@yahoo.com
FB| African Imports Houston
IG| obility12

Melodrama Boutique
Address| 5306 Almeda Rd, Houston, TX
77004, US
Hours| Thurs-Sat 2pm-6pm | Sun: Closed
Phone| 713-523-1608
Price range| $$-$$$
Email| melodrama.boutique@gmail.com
Website| www.melodramaboutique.com/
FB| Melodrama Boutique
IG| Melodramaboutique

JACKSON| FLORIDA

Meow and Barks Boutique
Address| 1537 San Marco Blvd,
Jacksonville, FL 32207
Hours| Tues-Fri: 10:30am-7:30pm
Sat:10am-6:30pm
Sun-Mon:Closed
Phone| 904-704-8222
Price range| $$-$$$
Size range| XS-3X
Email| rcarpet11@yahoo.com
Website| www.meowandbarksboutique.
storenvy.com/products
FB| Meowandbarksboutique
IG| Meowandbarksboutique

LOS ANGELES| CALIFORNIA

Dena Burton Designs
Address| Los Angeles Apparel Mart
112 W. 9th St. Suite 319
Los Angeles, CA 90035
Phone| 310-853-0852
Hours| By Appointment Only
Price Range| $-$$$$
Size Range| XS-3X
Email| denaburton@denaburton.com
Website| www.denaburton.com
FB| Dena Burton Collection
IG| @denaburton

No Body Jones Boutique
Address| 5593 W. Pico Blvd,
  Los Angeles, California 90019
Hours| Tues-Sat: 11am-7pm | Sun:
  11am-5pm
Phone| 323-291-7177
Email| nobodyjonesinfo@aol.com
Price range| $$-$$$
Size range| XS-3X
Website| www.nobodyjones.com
FB| Nobody Jones Boutique
IG| Nobodyjonesboutique

Queen Boutique
Address| 5011 W Pico Blvd,
  Los Angeles, CA 90019
Hours| Tues-Sat: 11am-5pm
Phone| 323-578-7724
Email| info@queenlosangeles.com
Website| www.queenlosangeles.com/
Price Range| $-$$$
Size Range| N/A
FB| Queen Boutique
IG| Queen Boutique

Zoe's Vintique
Address| 1410 South Redondo Blvd Los
  Angeles, CA 90019
Hours| Mon-Thurs: 11am-7pm | Fri-Sat:
  11am-8pm
Phone| 323-934-0302
Email| zoesvintique@gmail.com
Website| www.zoesvintique.com
Price Range| $-$$$$
Size Range| XS-4X
FB| Zoesvintique
IG| ZoesVintique

OAKLAND| CALIFORNIA

Taylor Jay Collection
Address| 2355 Broadway STE 1,
  Oakland, CA 94612
Hours| Tues-Sun: 12pm-6pm | Mon: By
  appointment
Phone| 1 242-601-3680
Price Range| $$-$$$
Size Range| XS-3X
Email| customerservice@
  taylorjaycollection.com
Website| www.taylorjaycollection.com/
FB| Taylor Jay Collection
IG| Shoptaylorjay

MILWAUKEE| WISCONSIN

Levine's Boutique
Address| 5510 W. Center ST,
  Milwaukee, WI 53210
Hours| Mon-Sat: 11:30am-6pm | Sun:
  Closed
Phone| 414- 459-1123
Email info@levinesboutique.com
Price Range| $-$$
Size Range| XS-3X
Website| www.levinesboutique.com/
FB| Levine's Consignment and Resale
  Boutique
IG| LevinesBoutique

PATERSON| NEW JERSEY

Gideon's Needle
Address| 221 Haledon Avenue,
  Paterson, NJ 07522
Hours| Mon-Fri: 9am-7pm EST | Sat:
  10am - 5pm (EST)
Phone| 862-336-1SEW (1739)
Email| info@gideonsneedle.com
Price Range| $$-$$$
Size Range| All Sizes
Website| www.gideonsneedle.com/
FB| Facebook.com/gideonsneedle
IG| gideonsneedleInternational

NASSAU| BAHAMAS

Rare Finds
Address| Prince George Plaza, Bay
  Street, Nassau,
  New Providence
Hours| Mon-Sat: 10:30am-6pm | Sun:
  10am-4pm island time
Phone| 242-601-3680
Email| hello@rarefindsbahamas.com
Price Range| $$-$$$
Size Range| XS-3X
Email| hello@rarefindsbahamas.com
Website| N/A
FB| RareFindsBoutique
IG| Rarefindsbahamas

LASHAWN B DESIGNS

FASHION IS ART AND YOU ARE THE CANVAS

LASHAWN B DESIGNS PUTS A CONTEMPORARY SPIN ON 70'S INSPIRED TRENDS, BOLD PATTERNS, AND SOPHISTICATED AND TIMELESS GARMENTS.

PHOTOGRAPHER | JUAN ANTHONY

WWW.LASHAWNBDESIGNS.COM

BODY FIGURE GUIDE

For many women, knowing their body type and how to dress it might come as a challenge. That's why I've decided to include this cheat sheet of body figure types to help women identify their body figures. Also included are a few figure-flattering garments to wear as style staples no matter what new trend is on the fashion scene. Let's take a look at the basic body types:

HOUR GLASS TYPE

Hourglass body types are defined by having both the bust and the hips proportional to each other with a slightly smaller waist. You generally have a full bust, bigger thighs and a rounded bottom and hips. An example of a celebrity sistah with an hourglass figure is the actress Halle Berry. If you are a true hourglass shape, the key is to accentuate your curves and not to hide them with oversized garments that do not define your waist. A few figure flattering fashion staples to consider on your next shopping trip are:

- Belted dresses and jackets such as wrap dresses and trench coats
- Low neckline tops and blouses such as a V-neck
- Pencils skirts and A-line skirts to flatter the curves
- Wide leg and boot cut pants with a belted waist tend to balance the hips
- Fabrics in knits and solid colors are also great for this body figure type

HOURGLASS

PEAR BODY TYPE

If you are a pear body shape, then you can probably relate to pop star singer/actress Beyoncé Knowles-Carter for having larger hips than both your bust and waist. You are defined by having a defined waist, shoulders that are narrower than your hips, and generally a small bust. Your waist usually flows out to your hips. If you know without a doubt that this is your body type, then try wearing these clothes to guarantee your best style and fit every time:

- Jackets & tops that finish above or below the hip line
- Wrap blouses are perfect for dressing up your top half can be fun with this body type by wearing volume such as puffed sleeves, cap sleeves, boleros, along with lots of color and patterns in addition to button down shirts and fitted t-shirts to balance your wide bottom half.
- Skirts and dresses are great for defining the waistline
- Wide leg pants also look great on you for this body type

TRIANGLE

INVERTED TRIANGLE

If you are a pear body shape, then you can probably relate to pop star singer/actress Beyoncé Knowles-Carter for having larger hips than both your bust and waist. You are defined by having a defined waist, shoulders that are narrower than your hips, and generally a small bust. Your waist usually flows out to your hips. If you know without a doubt that this is your body type, then try wearing these clothes to guarantee your best style and fit every time:

- Jackets & tops that finish above or below the hip line
- Wrap blouses are perfect for dressing up your top half can be fun with this body type by wearing volume such as puffed sleeves, cap sleeves, boleros, along with lots of color and patterns in addition to button down shirts and fitted t-shirts to balance your wide bottom half.
- Skirts and dresses are great for defining the waistline
- Wide leg pants also look great on you for this body type

INVERTED
TRIANGLE

113

STRAIGHT BODY TYPE

One of the most common super model body figure types is
the straight body type or some refer to it as the rectangular or
H-Ruler shaped body type. You are a straight body type when
both your bust and hips are the same size and your waist is
smaller than both of these. Usually you are defined by having
a small bust, small waist and flat hips and a bottom, as well as
straight shoulders and rib cage with little to no body curves.
Dressing for your shape can be both easy and fun. To dress
your body type, try wearing:

- Boat neck tops, wide V and U-necks
- Full, rush and flowing skirts --those with a nipped
  and belted waist
- Embellishments surrounding the bust and shoulders
  are great for adding volume on top
- Pants that are full or slightly flared legs, boot-cut and
  flared jeans, wide waistband pants and those with
  pockets, all for the sake of giving you the illusion of a
  curvy and well balanced bottom half

RECTANGLE

ROUND BODY TYPE

Last but not least, let's take a look at a very common body shape
among women --the round or apple body type. If you have this
shape, then you can probably relate to curvy celebrity sistahs such
as Queen Latifah. Your body is defined as being curvy all around
with a full or large bust, hips and a full midsection. More often,
you tend to gain weight in the stomach, back and upper body.
Dressing can become practical by wearing: balancing tops and
bottoms. For example:

- Flowy tops or those with nipped or belted waists
- Square, wide V and U-necks and vertical tops to help
  reduce perception of bust area
- Wrap style tops and jackets along with swing coats,
  especially those that flare at the hip, can help mask your
  tummy area
- Garments that can help to minimize your bottom such
  as full, tiered, flared or bubble skirts
- Pants with a mid-rise waist and wide waist bands, as
  well as those with full or wide legs
- Some of your strongest body assets are your shoulders
  and legs, so be sure to find those tops and skirts that I
  mentioned to help emphasize your figure highlights

ROUNDED

So there you have it. I've provided a brief overview of some of the top five body shapes common to women, however, there are other body types that havesurfaced in recent years that may offer you a more in depth look into your body type. I recommend Google for looking up body shapes; as you know, Google knows mostly everything.

I also recommend you search online for all of the different types of tops, skirts, jackets and pants I've mentioned, so you can get a visual picture of what to look for during your next boutique shopping trip around the Windy City.

Well, as for the fellas in your life, or if you are a guy with this book in your hand, please refer to the bibliography for links to common male body types.

FASHION GLOSSARY

I always say it's good to know the basic fashion components and terminology when out shopping. One of the things I've always been fascinated by is the different type of fibers that make up the everyday fabrics that you and I wear daily along with popular clothing silhouettes found in the fashion world. Check out this list to help you better understand the fashion world from the types popular style garments and everyday fashion jargon.

What are fibers?

Fibers are the threads of materials either natural or synthetic that are spun into yarn to produce our favorite Fabrics that we like to wear such as houndstooth, polka dots, gingham, plaid and so forth.

There are two categories of fibers: organic and synthetic.

Organic fibers are cotton, silk, wool, linen or flax, and some hair that come from plants or animals.

Some common **synthetic fibers** that we often wear are chemically manufactured including rayon, nylon, polyester, acrylic and acetate.

What are fabrics?

Fabrics consist of fibers that are woven, knitted, or crocheted. During shopping, you'll be able to tell if the garment is 100% natural, synthetic, or a mixture of both. Below, I have included a quick list of common fabrics and descriptions that we all love and are great conversation pieces when worn everyday, or while attending a special occasion such as parties, weddings, and black tie events.

Acrylic- A man made fabric created as a synthetic wool and cotton and is often used to make sweaters during the colder season because of its heat insulating characteristics.

Chiffon- This fabric is a popular special occasion fabric characterized by its sheer soft, breathable lightweight attributes. It's usually made from a combination of natural fibers such as silk, and synthetic fibers such as polyester. Most evening dresses, blouses and summer bridal attire are made from this flowy fabric.

Cotton- Considered one of the most popular fabrics ever. Many fabrics are made from this natural fiber including denim, poplin, jersey, t-shirts, cable knits, and more! There's no escaping the fashion world without running into one of the many cotton fabrics.

Linen- Another natural fabric, linen is considered the world's strongest natural fiber for its long lasting durability. Made from the natural plant fiber flax, linen can be worn all seasons, but best worn in the summer because of its breathability and ability to help moisture move smoothly.

Organza- A predominantly social attire fabric, this light shear weight synthetic fabric, often made from polyester and nylon, is most commonly seen in evening wear, bridal gowns and fancy scarves. Unlike chiffon, this fabric is stiff and dull or matte in appearance, and great for dresses that are more structured than flowy ones.

Polyester- Considered one of the workhorse fabrications of all times primarily because of its non-shrinkage and anti- wrinkle abilities, resistance to stretching, and ability to dry quicker than most fabrics. This synthetic fabric can be found in your favorite clothing such as t-shirts, blouses, home linens, pillows, curtains, you name it! Polyester is always somewhere on the fashion and home textile scenes.

Silk- Just like cotton, this natural fiber is a classic fabric well known for its smooth touch and is, to-date, still coined the most luxurious fabric on the planet. Most eveningwear and lingerie are made from silk fabrics.

Taffeta- One of my favorite fabrics to see and touch, is a twisted textured woven fabric similar to satin, but not as glossy. You've probably seen this fabric on beautiful ballroom gowns; bridal and evening wear, including fancy full skirts.

www.42explore.com/fibers.htm
www.regalfabricgallery.com/what-are-you-wearing-today/
www.regalfabricgallery.com/

<u>Common Fashion Terminology</u>

Classic Fashion- long-lasting fashion silhouettes, clothing styles and colors that transcend time. An example is a little black dress in various styles such as an A-line dress, sheath or shift dress.

Trends- Trend fashion is fashion that is usually influential, popular style clothing that lasts for seasons and or several years. Popular influencers on the market and sometimes an altered classic. A good example is a single shouldered blouse, jumpsuit, or dress that may appear every two to three years or so within the market.

Fad- Not a term quite often used by everyday consumers, but means fashion that is typically novelty driven and fades as quickly as it appears within the fashion industry. It's a jump on the bandwagon fashion term. One good example of a clothing item that was a recent fad was the rise and disappearance of the bodycon dresses with cut out backs, or another fad style is cut out shoulder dresses.

Must Know Fashion Hierarchy Terminology
What's the difference between couture, designer, and ready-to-wear?

We often go shopping, or have watched popular entertainment and fashion shows such as Project Runway, or have heard of the fashion hierarchy: Haute couture, prêt-à-porter/ready-to-wear, and value market fashion thrown around. But, what exactly are the meanings behind these fashion levels? My goal is for you to walk away and never have to worry about understanding the difference between these fashion terms/hierarchies again. I'll start at the top:

Couture Fashion or Haute Couture is a French fashion term that means high-fashion in style and in price. It's usually characterized by a unique one-of-a-kind, custom designed garment not mass-produced or manufactured, that is often handmade with luxurious materials. It's the cream of the crop of all fashion levels. Most celebrities are spotted on the red carpet in exclusive unique one-of-a-kind high-fashion gowns or haute couture brands.

Prêt-à-porter is another French term that translates to mean "ready-to-wear" in fashion. These fashions are often the most consumed in that you can find them easily hanging on the rack in your favorite store, often in large quantities and ready for you to purchase and wear. They can be high or low quality garments at boutiques, specialty and department stores.

Avant-garde Fashion- Typically this fashion is out-of-the box or, as many like to call it, "unconventional fashion." Avante-garde is creative, experimental, innovative, and so out of the boundaries of what people would wear or accept as normal fashion.

Made to Measure- Just as it sounds –is clothing that is made with the intention to provide a greater fit for the wearer. Tailored suits are often made to measure, which really means the fashion may be made for a general standard size, but can be tailored or altered to flatter the buyer. This fashion can be a combination of machine and handsewn.

Bespoke- Of all the garments created this British fashion term for custom clothing is usually made to fit the buyer's measurements precisely. This fashion is often made of luxurious fabrics chosen by the customer and is usually handsewn by the designer to fit the buyer's unique specifications.

CHICAGO NEIGHBORHOOD MAP

CHICAGO

CHICAGOLAND MAP

Book Cover Background Image
Big Joe. Chicago Purple Skyline. www.istockphoto.com,
Boutique Key Guide Man & Woman Vector Images
Kritchanut. Men & Woman Vector Icon. www.123rg.com.

Boutique Key Guide Fashion Vector Images
comb, jewelry, lamp, perfume, shoes, bag, cosmetics www. Adobestock.com
Images © / Adobe Stock

Boutique Vintage Key Guide Vector
Ivanova, Elena, Vintage Icon. www.123rg.com.
Boutique Key Guide Kids Fashion Vector Image
Severyn, Vladyslav, Kids fashion vector. www.123rg.com.

Female Body Figure Type Illustrations
Ewelina, Kowalska. "Female Body Figure Types" www.123rg.com.
Book Interior Images

Bronzeville Boutique Interior photo pg. 26 Photo Courtesy of Treva Johnson
Jermikko Design Studio and Production interior photo pg. 40
Photo Courtesy of Jermikko Shoshanna, Photography Fred, Model Kai
Miami Paris Boutique interior photo pg. 43   photo courtesy of Miami Paris
Boutique
Gilda Designer Thrift Boutique photos pg. 46 courtesy of Gilda Norris Glam
Fashion Love Boutique
interior photo pg. 22 photo courtesy of Glam Fashion Love
The Frock Shop interior photo pg. 51 photo Courtesy of Jennifer Burrell
Shernett Swaby interior photo pg. 60 Photo Courtesy of Shernett Swaby
Perfect Pieces Interior Photo pg. Photo courtesy of Perfect Pieces
Closet Consignment Boutique Photos pg. 73 Courtesy of Classy Closet
Consignment Boutique
Get Eyed Boutique photos pg.74photo courtesy of Eye Boutique, Photo by Elijah
Haymer
Stepping out on Faith Consignment Shop interior photo pg.75Photo Courtesy
Stepping out on Faith
Consignment Shop
 Terese Fee Fe photos pg.77 Photos courtesy of Teresa Fe Fe Designs
Wired by Design Boutique Photos pg.78-79 photo Courtesy of Wired by Design
Boutique
Anjel Boutique photos pg. 77 photos courtesy of Anjel Boutique
Divine Soul Boutique photos pg. 80 Photos courtesy of Divine Soul Boutique
Lure Boutique photos pg. 87 Photos Courtesy of Lure Boutique
The Ladies Consignment Boutique photos pg. 88-89 The Ladies
Consignment Boutique

SELECTED BIBLIOGRAPHY

"Most Common Types of Fashion" www.regalfabrics.com, Regal Fabrics,
February 20, 2020, www.regalfabrics.com/fabrics-101/glossary/.

"Haute Couture, Ready-To-Wear, and Prêt-à-Porter", www.apparelsearch.com,
Apparel Search, November 1, 2017.

Lamb, Annette, and Larry Johnson. "Fiber and Fabric." January, 1999.
www.42explore.com/fibers.htm

"What's your body shape?" shopyourshape.com, Shop Your Shape, November 2,
2017.

Biswas, Charushila. "12 Different Body Shapes Of Women." Style Craze.
November 30, 2017
www.stylecraze.com/articles/different-body-shapes-of-women/#gref

Martin, Melanie Yvette. "Do You Know Your Body Type?" Ebony. June 17, 2013,
www.ebony.com/style/do-you-know-your-body-type-993/axzz4s-
33GWABX.

Collings, Kat. "The Complete Guide to Dressing for Your Body Type." November 1,
2017.
"Who What Wear." April 26, 2019.
www.whowhatwear.com/how-to-dress-for-body-type-pear-apple-
hourglass/slide14

"Female Body Shapes." November 1, 2017. www.peprimer.com/female-body-
shape.html#SECTION1

"The Guide to Bodyshapes: Overview." Joy of Clothes, November 2, 2017.
www.joyofclothes.com/style-advice/shape-guides/body-shapes-
overview.php

Bird, Blue. "Fads, Trends, & Classics." Fashion Cycles. February 24, 2012.
www.fashioncycles.blogspot.com/2012/02/fads-trends-classics.htm

INDEX
BY MERCHANDISE CATEGORIES

COSMETICS

Absolutely Anything Essential Gift Shop pg 25
Anjels Boutique pg 76
Bronzeville Boutique by Lady Mocha pg 26
Chic Chick's Boutique pg 91
Culture Closet Boutique pg 17
Dez De Mee House of Styles pg 18
Effortless Style Boutique pg 31
Ellana Boutique pg 37
Goree Shop pg 28
Kayra Imports pg 33
Lure Boutique pg 86
Momadou's Jewelry & Clothing pg 41
Perfect Fit Fashions pg 92
Rosebud Reflections pg 36
Pursenalaties pg 94
Stampleys Executive Salon pg 50
Suit Plus More pg 85

HAIR PRODUCTS/SALON

Absolutely Anything Essential Gift Shop pg 25
Bellē Up pg 16
Effortless Style Boutique pg 31
Kayra Imports pg 33
Momadou's Jewelry & Clothing pg 41
Rosebud Reflections pg 36
Pursenalaties pg 94
Stampleys Executive Salon pg 50
Suit Plus More pg 85

HOME GOODS/FURNTIURE

A Lot of Good Stuff pg 24
Chic Chick's Boutique pg 91
Gilda Designers Thrift Boutique pg 46
Goree Shop pg 28
Kayra Imports pg 33
Kiwis Boutique pg 56
Lure Boutique pg 86

MEN'S ACCESSORIES

A Lot of Good Stuff pg 24
Agriculture Custom Clothiers pg 44
Barbara Bates Designs pg 61
Borris Powell pg 68
Brims & Accessories pg 30
Classy Closet Consignment Boutique pg 72
Custom By Lamar pg 55
Fort Smith Boutique pg 27
Gilda Designers Thrift Boutique pg 46
Iridium Clothing pg 39
Island Furs pg 19
Jermikko Design Studios pg 40
Kayra Imports pg 33
Kham'ryn B. Shoes pg 14
Kilimanjaro International pg 47
Ladies and Gentlemen Boutique pg 89
Silver Room pg 48
Sir & Madam pg 49
Sole Resale Boutique pg 57
Taj B. Couture Fashion House pg 84

MEN'S FASHION

Agriculture Custom Clothiers pg 44
A Lot of Good Stuff pg 24
Barbara Bates Designs pg 61
Borris Powell pg 68
Brims & Accessories pg 30
Classy Closet Consignment Boutique pg 72
Custom By Lamar pg 56
Gilda Designers Thrift Boutique pg 46
Goree Shop pg 28
Iridium Clothing pg 39
Island Furs pg 19
Jermikko Design Studios pg 40
Kayra Imports pg 33
Kham'ryn B. Shoes pg 14
Kilimanjaro International pg 47
Kiwis Boutique pg 56
Ladies and Gentlemen Boutique pg 89
Silver Room pg 48
Sir & Madam pg 49
Sole Resale Boutique pg 57
Stepping out on Faith Consignment pg 74
Succezz pg 63
Suit Plus More pg 85
Sullivan's Fashions pg 66
Taj B. Couture Fashion House pg 84
Teresa Fe-Fe Designs pg 80
Wiired by Design Boutique

MEN'S SHOES

A Lot of Good Stuff pg 24
Brims & Accessories pg 30
Gilda Designers Thrift Boutique pg 46
Goree Shop pg 28
Kham'ryn B. Shoes pg 14
Ladies and Gentlemen Boutique pg 89
Sir & Madam pg 49
Sole Resale Boutique pg 57
Stepping out on Faith Consignment pg 74
Succezz pg 63
Teresa Fe-Fe Designs pg 80
Wesley Shoes pg 51

SPA/BODYPRODUCTS

Annie Bell Fragrances pg 70
Absolutely Anything Essential Gift Shop pg 25

A Lot of Good Stuff pg 24
Avant Garde Boutique pg 83
Bellē Up pg 16
Chic Chick's Boutique pg 91
Effortless Style Boutique pg 31
Ellana Boutique pg 37
Fort Smith Boutique pg 27
Goree Shop pg 28
Kayra Imports pg 33
Kilimanjaro International pg 47
Kiwis Boutique pg 56
Looks & Style pg 34
Momadou's Jewelry & Clothing pg 41
Rosebud Reflections pg 36
Pursenalaties pg 94
Sarah Kuenyefu pg 69
Sir & Madam pg 49

WOMEN'S FASHION & ACCESSORIES

Absolutely Anything Essential Gift Shop pg 25
A Lot of Good Stuff pg 24
Anjels Boutique pg 76
Avant Garde Boutique pg 83
Barbara Bates Designs pg 61
Bellē Up pg 16
Borris Powell pg 68
Bronzeville Boutique by Lady Mocha pg 26
Chic Chick's Boutique pg 91
Classy Closet Consignment Boutique pg 72
Custom By Lamar pg 55
Dez De Mee House of Styles pg 18
Divine Sole Boutique pg 81
Effortless Style Boutique pg 31
Ellana Boutique pg 37
Essential Elements pg 32
Eye Boutique pg 73
Fort Smith Boutique pg 27
Gilda Designers Thrift Boutique pg 46
Glam Fashion Love pg 22
Goree Shop pg 28
Hyfaluten Boutique pg 83
Iridium Clothing pg 39
Island Furs pg 19
Jermikko Design Studios pg 40
Kayra Imports pg 33
Kham'ryn B. Shoes pg 14
Kilimanjaro International pg 47
Kiwis Boutique pg 56
The Ladies Consignment Boutique pg 89
Ladies and Gentlemen Boutique pg 89
Let's Do It Again Resale pg 91
Looks & Style pg 34
Lure Boutique pg 86
Maxine's Boutique pg 35
Miami Paris Boutique pg 43
Momadou's Jewelry & Clothing pg 41

Ms Cat Walk pg 62
Perfect Fit Fashions pg 92
Perfect Pieces pg 65
Pmarie Bridal Salon pg 21
Momadou's Jewelry & Clothing pg 41
Pmarie Bridal Salon pg 21
Shernet Swaby pg 59
Pursenalaties pg 94
Rosebud Reflections pg 36
Sarah Kuenyefu pg 69
Shernet Swaby pg 59
Silver Room pg 48
Sir & Madam pg 49
Sole Resale Boutique pg 57
Stampleys Executive Salon pg 50
Stepping out on Faith Consignment pg 74
Style Room 326 pg 53
Succezz pg 63
Suit Plus More pg 85
Sullivan's Fashions pg 66
Taj B. Couture Fashion House pg 84
Teresa Fe-Fe Designs pg 80
The Ladies Room Consignment pg 87-88
Wiired by Design Boutique pg 77-78

WOMEN'S FULL FIGURED FASHIONS

A Lot of Good Stuff pg 24
Anjels Boutique pg 76
Avant Garde Boutique pg 83
Barbara Bates Designs pg 61
Bellē Up pg 16
Borris Powell pg 68
Bronzeville Boutique by Lady Mocha pg 26
Chic Chick's Boutique pg 91
Culture Closet Boutique pg 17
Classy Closet Consignment Boutique pg 72
Custom By Lamar pg 55
Dez De Mee House of Styles pg 18
Divine Sole Boutique pg 80
Effortless Style Boutique pg 31
Ellana Boutique pg 37
Essential Elements pg 32
Eye Boutique pg 73
Fort Smith Boutique pg 27
Gilda Designers Thrift Boutique pg 46
Glam Fashion Love pg 22
Goree Shop pg 28
Hyfaluten Boutique pg 83
Iridium Clothing pg 39
Island Furs pg 19
Jermikko Design Studios pg 40
Kayra Imports pg 33
Kham'ryn B. Shoes pg 14
Kilimanjaro International pg 47
Kiwis Boutique pg 56
The Ladies Room Consignment pg 87-88
Ladies and Gentlemen Boutique pg 89

Let's Do It Again Resale pg 91
Looks & Style pg 34
Lure Boutique pg 86
Maxine's Boutique pg 35
Momadou's Jewelry & Clothing pg 41
Ms.Cat Walk pg 63
Perfect Fit Fashions pg 92
Perfect Pieces pg 65
Pmarie Bridal Salon pg 21
Pursenalaties pg 94
Rosebud Reflections pg 36
Sarah Kuenyefu pg 69
Shernet Swaby pg 59
Silver Room pg 48
Sir & Madam pg 49
Sole Resale Boutique pg 57
Stampleys Executive Salon pg 50
Stepping out on Faith Consignment pg 74
Style Room 326 pg 53
Succezz pg 63
Suit Plus More pg 85
Sullivan's Fashions pg 66
Taj B. Couture Fashion House pg 84
Teresa Fe-Fe Designs pg 80
The Ladies Room Consignment pg 87-88
Wired The Design Boutique pg 77-78

WOMEN'S SHOES

A Lot of Good Stuff pg 24
Anjels Boutique pg 76
Avant Garde Boutique pg 83
Barbara Bates Designs pg 61
Bellē Up pg 16
Borris Powell pg 68
Bronzeville Boutique by Lady Mocha pg 26
Chic Chick's Boutique pg 91
Culture Closet Boutique pg 17
Classy Closet Consignment Boutique pg 72
Custom By Lamar pg 55
Dez De Mee House of Styles pg 18
Divine Sole Boutique pg 80
Effortless Style Boutique pg 31
Ellana Boutique pg 37
Essential Elements pg 32
Eye Boutique pg 73
Fort Smith Boutique pg 27
Gilda Designers Thrift Boutique pg 46
Glam Fashion Love pg 22
Goree Shop pg 28
Hyfaluten Boutique pg 83
Iridium Clothing pg 39
Island Furs pg 19
Jermikko Design Studios pg 40
Kayra Imports pg 33
Kham'ryn B. Shoes pg 14
Kilimanjaro International pg 47
Kiwis Boutique pg 56
The Ladies Room Consignment pg 87-88

Ladies and Gentlemen Boutique pg 89
Let's Do It Again Resale pg 91
Looks & Style pg 34
Lure Boutique pg 86
Maxine's Boutique pg 35
Momadou's Jewelry & Clothing pg 41
Ms.Cat Walk pg 63
Perfect Fit Fashions pg 92
Perfect Pieces pg 65
Pmarie Bridal Salon pg 21
Pursenalaties pg 94
Rosebud Reflections pg 36
Sarah Kuenyefu pg 69
Shernet Swaby pg 59
Silver Room pg 48
Sir & Madam pg 49
Sole Resale Boutique pg 57
Stampleys Executive Salon pg 50
Stepping out on Faith Consignment pg 74
Style Room 326 pg 53
Succezz pg 63
Suit Plus More pg 85
Sullivan's Fashions pg 66
Taj B. Couture Fashion House pg 84
Teresa Fe-Fe Designs pg 80
The Ladies Room Consignment pg 87-88
Wired The Design Boutique pg 77-78

BOUTIQUE INDEX
ALPHABETICALLY

A Lot of Good Stuff pg 24
Absolutely Anything Essential Gift Shop
pg 25
Africa Imports Houston pg 109
African Safari Imports pg 53
African Wonderland Imports pg 53
Afrikiko Hair and Fashion Boutique pg 53
Agriculture Custom Clothiers pg 44
Allyson Mari pg 14
Alpha & Omega pg 19
Anjels Boutique pg 76
Annie Bell Fragrances pg 70
Annies Accents pg 63
Avant Garde Boutique pg 83
Barbara Bates Designs pg 61
Bellē Up pg 16
Borris Powell pg 68
Boutique Envie pg 28
Brims & Accessories pg 30
Bronzeville Boutique by Lady Mocha pg 26
Brown Elephant Resale Shop pg 93
Brownstone Boutique NY pg 108
Calabar Imports pg 107
Cannon's T-Shirts & More pg 14

Chic Chick's Boutique pg 90
Classy Closet Consignment Boutique pg 72
Community Thrift Shop pg 36
Creme De la Creme Resale Shop pg 53
Culture Connection pg 14
Culture Closet Boutique pg 17
Custom By Lamar pg 55
Cynthia J Designs pg 108
Dena Burton Designs pg 109
Dez De Mee House of Styles pg 18
Divine Soul Boutique pg 79
Djenne Collection pg 19
Dye Hard Yarns pg 93
Effortless Style Boutique pg 31
Elegant Fashions pg 93
Ellana Boutique pg 37
Epyk Luxury Boutique pg 84
Essential Elements pg 32
Eye Boutique pg 73
Fashionably Unpredictable pg 56
Fort Smith Boutique pg 27
Gideon's Needle pg 110
Gilda Designers Thrift Boutique pg 46
Glam Fashion Love pg 22
Goree Shop pg 28
GQ Gentlemen Boutique pg 14
Harlem Haberdashery pg 108
Hobdy Shoe Repair pg 19
I'MarE Boutique pg 109
Iridium Clothing pg 39
Island Furs pg 19
Jermikko Design Studios pg 40
Kayra Imports pg 33
Keeping the Faith Boutique pg 84
Kham'ryn B. Shoes pg 14
Kido pg 63
Kilimanjaro International pg 47
Kiwis Boutique pg 56
Ladies and Gentlemen Boutique pg 89
Lady B. Boutique pg 53
Lakeside Treasures pg 53
Leaders 1354 pg 57
Legacy Men's Boutique pg 28
Let's Do It Again Resale pg 91
Levine's Boutique pg 110
Looks & Style pg 34
Lourdes Hats & Accessories pg 19
Lure Boutique pg 86
M Dramain pg 53
Marche Ru Dix pg 108
Maxine's Boutique pg 35
Melodrama Boutique pg 109
Meow and Barks Boutique pg 109
Miami Paris Boutique pg 43
Minouchic Boutique pg 74
Momadou's Jewelry & Clothing pg 41
Ms Cat Walk pg 62
Ms Elles's Especially Yours Boutique pg 108

Mystique Boutique pg 76
Nobody Jones Boutique pg 110
Perfect Fit Fashions pg 92
Perfect Pieces pg 65
Personal Privelage pg 57
Pink Sky Boutique pg 107
Pinke Junke Boutique pg 28
Pmarie Bridal Salon pg 21
Pressed pg 107
Queen Boutique pg 110
Rare Finds pg 110
Robi Girls Closet pg 109
Rosebud Reflections pg 36
Sarah Kuenyefu pg 69
Shernet Swaby pg 59
Shop 500 Boutique pg 51
Silver Room pg 48
Sir & Madam pg 49
Smartmove Furniture pg 28
Sole Resale Boutique pg 57
Stampleys Executive Salon pg 50
Stepping out on Faith Consignment pg 74
Studio144 pg 93
Style Eyes Optical pg 108
Style Room 326 pg 53
Succezz pg 63
Suit Plus More pg 85
Sullivan's Fashions pg 66
Tags Atlanta pg 107
Taj B. Couture Fashion House pg 84
Taylor Jay Collection pg 110
Teresa Fe-Fe Designs pg 80
The Fashion Revival Boutique pg 14
The House of Couture Houston pg 109
The Silver Umbrella pg 51
The Wrap Life pg 108
The Ladies Room Consignment pg 87-88
Unan Imports pg 53
V's Fashionable Boutique pg 93
Wesley Shoes pg 51
Wilbourn Sisters Designs pg 107
Wired The Design Boutique pg 77-78
Z Couture pg 66
Zion Wellness Center pg 65
Zoe's Vintique pg 110

THANK YOU FOR YOUR PURCHASE.
PLEASE, KINDLY LEAVE A BOOK REVIEW
ON AMAZON.COM AND WHEREVER YOU
PURCHASED THE BOOK ONLINE

-MB

Made in the USA
Monee, IL
23 August 2021